stylebook / editorial manual

Prepared by the
SCIENTIFIC PUBLICATIONS DIVISION
AMERICAN MEDICAL ASSOCIATION
William R. Barclay, MD, Director

Publishing Sciences Group, Inc.
Littleton, Massachusetts

FOREWORD

A scientific journal should have a consistency of style and an accuracy of reporting on which readers come to rely. The few rules a journal adapts should be simple, inviolable, and encourage clear, unambiguous writing.

This stylebook, in its sixth edition, incorporates changes in style and usage based on the experience of the AMA staff in our editorial office. It is primarily a guide for the AMA editorial staff but can be a valuable reference for any author who undertakes the writing of a medical scientific paper.

Emphasis is on the specific points of style currently in use in *JAMA* and the specialty journals of the AMA. We would be pleased to receive comments and suggestions from our many contributors on this edition and will give all suggestions serious consideration for publication in a subsequent edition.

SCIENTIFIC PUBLICATIONS DIVISION

CONTENTS

stylebook

A current criticism of medical articles is the overuse of abbreviations. The medical writer should avoid such overuse; if several abbreviations are to be used in an article, care should be taken not to confuse the reader. A saving in space can never justify a loss in comprehension. If doubt arises, abbreviations may be spelled out several times in a given article. (See also **12.00**, **14.14**, and **21.00**.)

1.01—**Periods**—All abbreviations are used without periods, except those of personal names. (See also **14.10**.)

AMA   MD   ECG   SGOT   US   WBC   PHS   CNS

IUD   ECFMG   USSR   VA   AMA-ERF   NIMH

mEq   pH   ml   rpm   mph

vol   mμ μg   pg

(*But:* John S. Smith, MD; W.B. Saunders Co, or abbreviations that are words in themselves [No.])

1.02—**Plurals**—No plural form is used for abbreviated units of measure. For all-cap abbreviations of other terms, the plural is formed by adding *s*. (See also **13.01**.)

50 mg   100 ml   4.5 mEq   400 cu mm   50 IU

ECGs   IQs   EEGs   IUDs   RBCs

See *Webster's* for correct plurals of other abbreviations.

Drs   pp   ff   Messrs   Mss

Do use the plural form of spelled out units of measure.

2.5 liters/24 hr   twenty-five milligrams

1.03—**Specialized Abbreviations**—These may be used, provided they (1) are not abbreviations of weight or measure, (2) do not involve a drug with a generic name,* (3) do not replace a standard abbreviation already in existence, and (4) are spelled out in full the first time, with the abbreviation following immediately in parentheses.

*LSD is an exception.

1.04—**Genus and Species**—After the singular form of the genus is mentioned once in the text, it should be abbreviated thereafter without a period when accompanied by the species name, even when the species is other than that given at first mention or when another genus has been mentioned in the interim. Use a genus abbreviation of more than one letter only when necessary to avoid ambiguity. Do not abbreviate the genus name when used alone without species. Do not abbreviate the species name. (See also **10.07.**)

Salmonella worthington, Shigella rio, and *Sal poona*

Pasteurella pfaffii, Pseudomonas sesami, and *Ps pisi*

1.05—**Names of Persons**—Given names should not be abbreviated except by initials. Do not use Chas., Jas., Jno., etc, except as part of the name of a company or organization that regularly uses such an abbreviation (**1.08**). Initials used for names of persons (usually coauthors of an article) should be followed by periods and set close.

One of us (R.H.C.) also studied this problem in Tanganyika.

Senior and *junior* are abbreviated when part of a name; they follow the surname and are set off by commas. (*But:* See **11.11, 15.08.**)

Peter Meter, Jr, saw James A. Ames, Sr, in New York.
(*But:* John Doe II)

1.06—**Titles of Persons**—Most titles (except military) are abbreviated only when they precede the full name (first name [or initials] and surname) of a person. Spell them out (1) when used before the surname alone, (2) at the beginning of a sentence, and (3) when used after a name. Abbreviations for military titles, and rules for their use, are given in **1.19.** For capitalization of titles, see **4.02.**

Superintendent Smith   Supt H.B. Smith

Henry B. Smith, superintendent

Col John G. Smith, MC, USA   Colonel Smith

Mr, Mrs, Ms, and *Dr* are always abbreviated when preceding a surname, with or without first name or initials.

Note: In most instances the title *Dr* should be used only after the specific degree (eg, MD, PhD, DVM, ScD) has been mentioned. (See example in **1.07.**)

The Reverend, Reverend, or *Rev* is used only when first name or initials are given with the surname. When only the surname is given, use *Mr* (or *Dr*), *the Reverend Mr* (or *Dr*) or *Father* (Roman Catholic, sometimes Anglican). (Never use *the Reverend Brown,* or *Reverend Brown,* or *Rev Brown*—not even in a footnote!)

1.07—**Academic Degrees**—Use abbreviations in accordance with the examples given.

ABBREVIATIONS

Arvin P. Clamp, MD, PhD, gave the opening address. At the close of the meeting, Dr Clamp was named permanent chairman of the committee.

Dr Caldwell was awarded an honorary degree of doctor of philosophy. Although he holds a PhD in mathematics, he is a doctor of medicine.

She received a bachelor's degree in 1962 and a master's in 1965; she will receive her HsD (doctor in health sciences) in the fall.

(*But:* Honorary degrees are not used in by-lines)

1.08—**Names of Business Firms**—Use the name of a company as the company uses it, but in footnotes and references, abbreviate *company, corporation, brothers, incorporated,* and *limited,* even if the company expands them. (See also **14.04/3.**)

John B. Ross & Co, Inc   Gale-Sharpe Corp

Richardson-Merrell Inc   Smith Kline & French Laboratories

Williams & Wilkins Co

1.09—**"United States" and "Department"**—When used as a noun, United States is written out; when preceding a noun as a modifier, it is abbreviated.

population of the United States

US government

In the names of government agencies, *US* is used only for departments and independent agencies; it is not used with the names of agencies within departments.

US Department of Health, Education, and Welfare

Public Health Service

As part of the title of a government agency, *department* is spelled out in the text and footnotes, abbreviated (Dept) in references.

1.10—**"Saint" and "Saints"**—Abbreviate as part of a proper name.

St Louis   St Andrew's Church

SS Peter and Paul   Sault Ste Marie

1.11—**States, Territories, Possessions**—Names should be spelled in full when standing alone. When they follow the name of a city, abbreviations should be used, without periods, without space between the letters. With zip codes, use postal codes.

ABBREVIATIONS

State	Abbreviation	Postal Code
Alabama	Ala	AL
Alaska	Alaska	AK
Arizona	Ariz	AZ
Arkansas	Ark	AR
California	Calif	CA
Canal Zone	Canal Zone	CZ
Colorado	Colo	CO
Connecticut	Conn	CT
Delaware	Del	DE
District of Columbia	DC	DC
Florida	Fla	FL
Georgia	Ga	GA
Guam	Guam	GU
Hawaii	Hawaii	HI
Idaho	Idaho	ID
Illinois	Ill	IL
Indiana	Ind	IN
Iowa	Iowa	IA
Kansas	Kan	KS
Kentucky	Ky	KY
Louisiana	La	LA
Maine	Me	ME
Maryland	Md	MD
Massachusetts	Mass	MA
Michigan	Mich	MI
Minnesota	Minn	MN
Mississippi	Miss	MS
Missouri	Mo	MO
Montana	Mont	MT
Nebraska	Neb	NE
Nevada	Nev	NV
New Hampshire	NH	NH
New Jersey	NJ	NJ
New Mexico	NM	NM
New York	NY	NY
North Carolina	NC	NC
North Dakota	ND	ND
Ohio	Ohio	OH
Oklahoma	Okla	OK
Oregon	Ore	OR
Pennsylvania	Pa	PA
Puerto Rico	Puerto Rico	PR
Rhode Island	RI	RI
South Carolina	SC	SC
South Dakota	SD	SD
Tennessee	Tenn	TN
Texas	Tex	TX
Utah	Utah	UT
Vermont	Vt	VT
Virginia	Va	VA

ABBREVIATIONS

Virgin Islands	Virgin Islands	VI
Washington	Wash	WA
West Virginia	WVa	WV
Wisconsin	Wis	WI
Wyoming	Wyo	WY

Do not abbreviate a state name after a county name.

Cook County, Illinois

1.12—**Cities**—Where there is no danger of confusion, the following cities may usually be mentioned without the name of the state, province, or country:

Amsterdam	Hiroshima	Omaha
Atlanta	Honolulu	Oslo
Baltimore	Houston	Ottawa
Belfast	Indianapolis	Paris
Berlin	Iowa City	Peking
Boston	Jerusalem	Philadelphia
Brussels	Las Vegas	Pittsburgh
Budapest	Leningrad	Prague
Buenos Aires	Lisbon	Quebec
Buffalo	London	Rio de Janeiro
Cairo	Los Angeles	Rome
Calcutta	Louisville	St Louis
Chicago	Madrid	St Paul
Cincinnati	Melbourne	Salt Lake City
Cleveland	Memphis	San Diego
Copenhagen	Mexico City	San Francisco
Dallas	Miami	Seattle
Denver	Milwaukee	Shanghai
Detroit	Minneapolis	Singapore
Dublin	Montreal	Stockholm
Edinburgh	Moscow	Tokyo
Geneva	Naples	Toronto
Guatemala City	New Delhi	Vienna
The Hague	New Orleans	Warsaw
Havana	New York	
Helsinki	Oklahoma City	

(*But:* London, Ontario; Moscow, Idaho; Naples, Fla; Vienna, Va)

Cities are not included in by-lines.

1.13—**Place Names in Names of Organizations**—When the name of a state is included in the name of an organization, it is not necessary to repeat the state name after the city, except when the zip code is also given, in which case the postal code is used.

University of Michigan, Ann Arbor

ABBREVIATIONS

Pennsylvania Department of Welfare, Harrisburg

University of Wisconsin, Madison, WI 53706

University of California at Davis

When a place name is included in the name of a hospital or other organization, the state name may be enclosed in parentheses after the place name and further designation of place and state may be omitted, *except* when a specific mailing address is given, as for reprints. (See also **14.09/2.**)

Winter Park (Fla) Memorial Hospital

1.14—**Local Addresses**—When complete local addresses are given, use the following abbreviations:

Ave   Bldg   Blvd   Ct   Dr   Hwy   Pl   Rd

St   Pkwy   Terr

When the plural is used, do not abbreviate (or capitalize) *streets, avenues,* etc. *Lane* is not abbreviated. Abbreviate *building* only when a building number or room number is given. First through Tenth streets are spelled out; numerals are used for 11th and above. Use suffixes: 21st, 32nd, 43rd. Use no periods with *N, S, E, W,* or combinations; use no commas before *SE, SW, NE, NW.*

Bldg 10, Room 10 D-18 (National Institutes of Health)

Elm and E 54th Streets   123 Indiana Ave SE

Cherry Lane at Hampton Court

PO Box 35620

1.15—**Months**—Abbreviate (except March, April, May, June, July) when day is used, with or without year. When no day is given, month is not abbreviated. (See also **14.04/8.**)

Nov 2   Dec 7, 1941   July 4, 1776   October 1929

1.16—**Days of Week**—Do not abbreviate, except in tables.

the following Friday   on Monday, Jan 16

1.17—**Beginning a Sentence**—At the beginning of a sentence, or when following a spelled-out number at the beginning of a sentence (**11.05**), what would ordinarily be abbreviated is written out.

Exceptions: (1) some titles of persons (**1.06; 1.19**), and (2) in reports of clinical data or laboratory study, a repeated abbreviation for a cumbersome technical phrase, eg, *SGOT.*

Four milliliters of blood was drawn.

But some sentences must be reworded to avoid beginning with an abbreviation:

Wrong: pH is the symbol for hydrogen ion concentration.

Right: The symbol for hydrogen ion concentration is pH.

1.18—**Journals**—In references, abbreviate the names of journals according to the listing in *Index Medicus,* except for variations as noted in **15.14.** (See also **15.02.**)

1.19—**Military Titles**—Abbreviate before surname when given name or initial is also used, in accordance with the listing below. (*Note:* In by-lines and signatures of signed communications [eg, LETTERS] military title precedes the name, military service follows the name.)

US Army

general of the army	GA
chief warrant officer	CW
warrant officer	WO

US Army, Air Force, and Marine Corps

general	Gen
lieutenant general	Lt Gen
major general	Maj Gen
brigadier general	Brig Gen
colonel	Col
lieutenant colonel	Lt Col
major	Maj
captain	Capt
first lieutenant	1st Lt
second lieutenant	2d Lt

US Navy*

fleet admiral	FADM
chief warrant officer	CWO

US Navy and Coast Guard

admiral	Adm
vice admiral	Vice Adm
rear admiral	Rear Adm
captain	Capt
commander	Comdr
lieutenant commander	Lt Comdr
lieutenant	Lt
lieutenant (junior grade)	Lt (jg)
ensign	Ens
warrant officer	WO

*Commodore is no longer used in the US Navy.

ABBREVIATIONS

1.20—**Military Services**—Abbreviations are as follows:

MC, USAF	United States Air Force Medical Corps
MC, USA	United States Army Medical Corps
MC, USN	United States Navy Medical Corps
USA	United States Army
USAF	United States Air Force
USCG	United States Coast Guard
USMC	United States Marine Corps
USN	United States Navy
USAR	United States Army Reserve
USAFR	United States Air Force Reserve
USCGR	United States Coast Guard Reserve
USMCR	United States Marine Corps Reserve
USNR	United States Naval Reserve

1.21—**Units of Measure**—Use these abbreviations and symbols with numerical quantity in accordance with **21.00**, and with virgule in accordance with **14.14**, except as otherwise specified here. They should not be expanded except as noted here and in **1.17**. (See also **1.01**.)

acre	Do not abbreviate
ampere	amp
Angstrom	A
atmosphere, standard	atm
Bessey-Lowry units	Do not abbreviate
billion electron volts	bev
Bodansky unit	BU*
British thermal unit	BTU
calorie	Do not abbreviate
candela	cd*
Celsius, centigrade	C
centigram	cg*
centimeter	cm
centipoise	cp*
coulomb	coul
cubic centimeter	cc (Use ml for liquid measure)
cubic foot	cu ft
cubic inch	cu in
cubic meter	cu m
cubic micron	cuμ
cubic millimeter	cu mm
cubic yard	cu yd
curie	Ci
cycles per second	cps
day	Do not abbreviate
decibel	dB

*Use abbreviation after spelling out the first time *without* abbreviation in parentheses.

ABBREVIATIONS

decigram	(Convert to grams)
deciliter	(Convert to milliliters)
decimeter	(Convert to meters)
degree (angle)	(Do not use with temperatures; see **11.03L**)
diopter	D*
dram	Do not abbreviate (See **21.04**)
dyne	Do not abbreviate
electron volt	eV
electrostatic unit	ESU*
equivalent roentgen	Do not abbreviate
farad (electric capacitance)	Do not abbreviate
Fahrenheit	F
fluid ounce (volume)	fl oz
foot	ft
foot-candle	ft-c*
foot-pound	ft-lb
foot-lambert	Do not abbreviate
gallon	gal
gas volume	Do not abbreviate
gas volume per unit time	V̊
grain	Do not abbreviate (See **21.04**)
gram	gm
gravity	g
henry (electric inductance)	H*
hertz	Hz
horsepower	hp
hour	hr†
immunizing unit	ImmU*
inch	in
international benzoate unit	IBU*
international milliunit	ImU
international unit	IU
intraocular pressure	IOP*
joule	Do not abbreviate
Kelvin (or Kelvin scale)	K
kilocalorie	kcal
kilocurie	kCi
kilocycle	kc
kiloelectron volt	keV
kilogram	kg
kilohertz	kHz
kilometer	km

†Use only in a virgule construction and in tables.

11

kilovolt	kV
kilovolt-ampere	kV (amp)
kilovolt (constant potential)	kV(cp)*
kilovolt (peak)	kV(p)*
kilowatt	kW
King-Armstrong unit	Do not abbreviate
knot	Do not abbreviate
liter	Do not abbreviate
lumen	Do not abbreviate
lux	Do not abbreviate
megacurie	MCi
megacycle	Mc
megahertz	MHz
megaunits (1 million units)	Do not abbreviate
meter	m
metric ton (tonne)	Do not abbreviate
microampere	μamp
microcurie	μCi
microfarad	Do not abbreviate
microgram	μg
microliter	μl
micrometer	(Use micron)
micromicrocurie	(Use picocurie; see **21.02**)
micromicrogram	(Use picogram; see **21.02**)
micromicron	$\mu\mu$
micromole	μmole
micron	μ
micromolar	μM
micronormal	μN
microosmol	μOsm
microunit	μU
microvolt	μV
microwatt	μW
mile	Do not abbreviate
miles per hour	mph
milliampere	mamp
millicurie	mCi
millicuries destroyed	mCid*
milliequivalent	mEq
millifarad	Do not abbreviate
milligram	mg
milligram-element	mg-el*
milliliter	ml
millimeter	mm
millimicrogram	mμg
millimicromolar	mμM
millimicron	mμ
millimicron equivalent (physical)	mμEq*
millimole	mmole

millimolar	mM
million electron volts	meV
milliosmol	mOsm
millirem	mrem
milliroentgen	mR
millisecond	msec
milliunit	mU
millivolt	mV
milliwatt	mW
minute (time)	min†
molar	M
mole	Do not abbreviate
month	mo†
mouse unit	MU
nanocurie	nCi
nanogram	ng
nanometer	nm
nanomole	nmole
newton	Do not abbreviate
normal (solution)	N (See 21.05)
ohm	Ω
ounce	oz
outflow (weight)	C*
oxygen consumption	Vo₂
parts per million	ppm
picocurie	pCi
picogram	pg
pint	pt
pound	lb
pounds per square inch	psi
pounds per square inch absolute	psia*
pounds per square inch gauge	psig*
prism diopter	PD, Δ
quart	qt
rad	Do not abbreviate
radian	Do not abbreviate
rat unit	RU*
revolutions per minute	rpm
roentgen	R
roentgen equivalents man (or mammal)	rem
roentgen equivalents physical	rep
Saybolt seconds universal	SSU*
second	sec†
siemens	Do not abbreviate
square centimeter	sq cm
square foot	sq ft
square inch	sq in

square meter	sq m
square millimeter	sq mm
Svedberg flotation unit	S_f*
threshold limit value	TLV
tonne (metric ton)	Do not abbreviate
tuberculin unit	TU
turbidity-reducing unit	TRU*
unit	Do not abbreviate
volt	V
volume percent	vol%
volume for volume	v/v
watt	W
week	wk†
weight for weight	w/w
yard	yd
year	yr†

1.22—**Clinical, Technical, and General Terms**—Use abbreviations in titles, illustrations, legends, and tables without expansion, except as otherwise specified. (See also **1.03**.) For additional abbreviations consult *Current Medical Information and Terminology* (AMA), *Council of Biology Editors Style Manual* (published for the council by the American Institute of Biological Sciences), *Medical Abbreviations* (Michigan Occupational Therapy Association), and library resources.

adenosine triphosphate	ATP*
adenosine triphosphatase	ATPase*
albumin-globulin ratio	A/G ratio*
alternating current	ac
alum-precipitated toxoid	APT*
American Hospital Association	AHA†
American Medical Association	AMA†
American Standards Association	ASA†
aminosalicylic acid	Do not abbreviate
angiocardiography	ACG*
anno Domini	AD
ante meridiem	AM
anteroposterior	AP†
antihemophilic globulin	AHG*
aortic second sound	A_2
approximately	approx‡
Association of American Medical Colleges	AAMC†
average	av‡

* Expand at first mention, with abbreviation immediately following in parentheses.
† Expand at first mention, without giving abbreviation parenthetically.
‡ Use only in tables.

basal metabolic rate	BMR*
before Christ	BC
before Christian era	BCE
bicolor guaiac test	Do not abbreviate
black (race)	B‡
blood pressure	BP*
blood urea nitrogen	BUN
body surface area	BSA*
boiling point	Do not abbreviate
British Pharmacopoeia	Do not abbreviate
carbon dioxide pressure (tension)	Pco_2
carbon dioxide pressure (tension), arterial	$Paco_2$
central nervous system	CNS
cerebrospinal fluid	CSF
Chick-cell agglutination	CCA*
chi square	χ^2(Gk 47)
circa	c
clearance, inulin	C_{IN}*
clearance, *p*-aminohippuric acid	C_{PAH}*
coefficient of variation	CV*
compare	cf
complement fixation test	CFT*
complete blood cell count	CBC*
convulsive shock therapy	CST*
creatine (creatinine) phosphokinase	CPK*
cerebrovascular accident	CVA*
cylinder	cyl (Use only in refraction formulas)
degrees of freedom	*df*
deoxycorticosterone	DOC*
deoxycorticosterone acetate	DOCA*
deoxycorticosterone glucoside	DOCG*
deoxyephedrine hydrochloride	DOE*
deoxyribonucleic acid	DNA
department	Dept (See **1.09**)
Department of Health, Education, and Welfare	DHEW*
deuterium	Do not abbreviate
dilation and curettage	D&C*
direct current	dc
doctor of dental medicine	DMD
doctor of dental surgery	DDS
doctor of medicine	MD
doctor of osteopathy	DO
doctor of pharmacy	PharmD
doctor of philosophy	PhD
doctor of podiatry	PodD

doctor of public health	DPH
doctor of science	ScD, DSc
doctor of veterinary medicine	DVM
double vibrations	dv*
ear, left	AS*
ear, right	AD*
ear, eye, nose, and throat	EENT*
ear, nose, and throat	ENT*
ectopic atrial beats	EAB
ectopic ventricular beats	EVB
edition, editor	ed
effective direct radiations	EDR*
effective dose for 50% of group	ED_{50}
electrocardiogram, electrocardiographic	ECG
electroencephalogram, electroencephalographic	EEG
electromotive force	EMF*
electromyogram	EMG*
electronystagmogram	ENG*
electro-oculogram	EOG*
electroshock therapy	EST*
erythrocyte sedimentation rate	ESR
et alii (et alius)	et al
et cetera	etc
exempli gratia	eg
experimenter	E*
extrasensory perception	ESP*
extremely high frequency	EHF*
eye, each; or both eyes	OU*
eye, left	OS*
eye, right	OD*
female	F‡
figure (figures)	Fig (Use only with numerical designation.) (See **8.01**.)
fluorescent treponemal antibody absorption test	FTA-ABS
focus-to-film distance	FFD*
focus-to-skin distance	FSD*
following, the following	ff (annotations only)
Food and Drug Administration	FDA†
forced inspiratory oxygen	FIO_2*
French catheter	F (Use only with a number)
frequency	f (statistics, formulas only)
galvanic skin response	GSR*
gastroenterology	GE*
gastrointestinal	GI*

ABBREVIATIONS

genitourinary	GU*
graduate in pharmacy	PharmG
half-value layer	HVL*
health maintenance organization	HMO†
hearing distance	HD*
hematocrit	Hct†
hemoglobin	Hb† (Use only with blood type designation)
high frequency	HF*
high power	HP*
high-power field	HPF*
House, Tree, Person (test)	HTP*
hydrogen-ion concentration	pH
idiopathic thrombocytopenic purpura	ITP*
infective dose	ID*
infrared	Do not abbreviate
intelligence quotient	IQ
International Standards Organization	ISO*
intramuscular	IM*
intrauterine (contraceptive) device	IUD*
intravenous	IV*
intravenous pyelogram	IVP*
Joint Commission on the Accreditation of Hospitals	JCAH*
kidneys, ureters, bladder	KUB*
lactic dehydrogenase	LDH*
left	L‡
lethal dose	LD*
lethal dose for 50% survival of group	LD$_{50}$*
licensed practical nurse	LPN
low frequency	LF*
low power	LP*
lupus erythematosus	LE*
lysergic acid diethylamide	LSD
male	M‡
manuscript, manuscripts	MS, MSS
master of public health	MPH
master of science	MS
master of surgery	ChM, MS
maximum	max‡
mean corpuscular hemoglobin	MCHb*

ABBREVIATIONS

mean corpuscular volume	MCV*
median	Do not abbreviate
Medical Education for National Defense	MEND*
meta	*m* (Use only in chemical formulas)
metabolic rate	MR*
minimum effective concentration	MEC*
minimal effective dose	MEfD*
minimal erythemal dose	MErD*
minimal inhibitory concentration	MIC*
minimal inhibitory dose (level)	MID(L)*
minimum lethal dose	MLD*
Minnesota Multiphasic Personality Inventory	MMPI*
mode	Do not abbreviate
molecular weight	mol wt*
multiple sclerosis	MS*
National Aeronautics and Space Administration	NASA*
National Cancer Institute	NCI*
National Eye Institute	NEI*
National Formulary	*NF**
National Heart and Lung Institute	NHLI*
National Institute of Allergy and Infectious Diseases	NIAID*
National Institute of Arthritis and Metabolic Diseases	NIAMD*
National Institute of Child Health and Human Development	NICHD*
National Institute of Dental Research	NIDR*
National Institute of Environmental Health Sciences	NIES*
National Institute of General Medical Sciences	NIGMS*
National Institutes of Health	NIH*
National Institute of Mental Health	NIMH*
National Institute of Neurological Diseases and Stroke	NINDS*
National Library of Medicine	NLM*
nonprotein nitrogen	NPN*
nonvolatile	nv*
normal temperature and pressure	NTP*
not significant	NS‡
number	No.
occupational therapy	OT*
oculus dexter (right eye)	OD
oculus sinister (left eye)	OS

oculus uterque (both eyes)	OU
old tuberculin	OT*
ortho	o- (Use only in chemical formulas)
oxygenated hemoglobin	HbO_2
oxygen consumption	QO_2
oxygen pressure (tension)	Po_2
oxygen pressure (tension), arterial	Pao_2
packed cell volume	PCV*
page, pages	p, pp (parenthetical annotations, references only)
p-aminosalicylic acid	Do not abbreviate
Papanicolaou (smear or test)	Do not abbreviate
para	p- (Use only in chemical formulas)
paralytic dose	PD_{00}*
paroxysmal nocturnal hemoglobinuria	PNH*
part	pt (references only)
periodic acid, Schiff	PAS
percentile	Do not abbreviate
plasma thromboplastin component	PTC*
pneumoencephalogram	PEG*
post meridiem	PM
post office	PO (Use only with box number)
premature atrial beat	PAB
premature ventricular beat	PVB
probability	P (Use only with numerical value)
Professional Standards Review Organization	PSRO†
protein-bound iodine	PBI*
Public Health Service	PHS†
pulmonary venous capillary	PVC*
pulmonic second sound	P_2*
purified protein derivative	PPD*
rapid eye movement	REM*
receptor-destroying enzyme	RDE*
red blood cell	RBC
registered pharmacist	RPh
relative biologic effectiveness (radiation)	RBE*
ribonucleic acid	RNA
serum glutamic oxaloacetic transaminase	SGOT
serum glutamic pyruvic transaminase	SGPT
skin erythemal dose	SErD*

ABBREVIATIONS

skin unit dose	SUD*
Social Security Administration	SSA†
source-skin distance	SSD*
standard deviation	SD or σ
standard error	SE
standard error of the mean	SEM
Student American Medical Association (American Medical Student Association)	SAMA (AMSA)†
summation	Σ
supplement	suppl (references only)
Surgeon General	Do not abbreviate
tertiary	*tert-* (Use only in chemical formulas)
Thematic Apperception Test	TAT*
tissue culture dose	TCD_{00}*
tissue culture infective dose	$TCID_{00}$*
Treponema pallidum complement fixation test	TPCF*
Treponema pallidum immobilization test	TPI*
tubular reabsorption of phosphate	TRP*
ultrahigh frequency	UHF*
United Nations	UN†
United States Pharmacopeia	USP†
US Department of Health, Education, and Welfare	DHEW†
valvular disease of the heart	VDH*
venereal disease	VD*
venereal disease, syphilis	VDS*
VDRL (test for syphilis)	Do not expand
versus	vs
Very high frequency	VHF
Veterans Administration	VA†
Wechsler Adult Intelligence Scale	WAIS*
Wechsler Intelligence Scale for Children	WISC*
weight by volume	W/V* (Use only with numbers.)
white (race)	W‡
white blood cell	WBC
World Health Organization	WHO†
World War I	WW I†
World War II	WW II†

Accent marks tend to be superfluous for persons whose first language is English. Words once spelled with marks (eg, coöperation, rôle) now are written and printed without them. The current trend toward omission of accent marks is given further impetus by the limitations of computer printing, by the additional cost in time and effort for marking copy, and by the increased likelihood of error when accents are used. Late-edition dictionaries give optional forms for words to show that they may or may not include accents (eg, resume / resumé / résumé; facade / façade).

2.01—Except in those instances where current usage continues inclusion of accent marks (diacritics), such marks normally should be omitted. If an author is consistent and insistent about use of accents with given terms, however, the accents may be retained.

Terms from which accents may be omitted:

Angstrom [Ångstrom]

Bekesy [Békésy]

cafe-au-lait [café-au-lait]

Meniere disease [Ménière disease]

Appropriate uses of accents:

To show pronunciation:

lues   (lü- ēz)

To show correct spelling in original language:

Köln (Cologne)

In quotations:

La parole a été donnée à l'homme pour déguiser sa pensée. [Speech has been given to man to conceal his thoughts.]

In terms where the accent is retained in current use:

garçon

Möbius strip [alternate form: Moebius]

tête-à-tête

2.02—Accents should be clearly marked on copy. Although for most typefaces the dieresis and umlaut are indistinguishable, each should be marked correctly.

Identification	*Example*
acute	le déluge

breve	Omskiĭ
cedilla	garçon
circumflex	tête-bêche
wedge	Čechoslovaca
dieresis	naïve
dot	faúst
grave	après
macron	gignōskein
ring	Ångstrom
slash	København, Społka
tilde	mañana
umlaut	für

BY-LINES—3.00

3.01—In all major contributions, authorship is indicated by a by-line, which appears immediately below the title. The by-line should contain (1) each author's first name, middle initial (or first initial and middle name), and surname, and (2) highest academic degrees (**3.02**) held by each author. Generally, the maximum number of authors' names in the by-line is six.

A. Arthur Sugerman, MD, Charles G. Clark, MD

3.02—If an author holds two doctoral degrees (eg, MD and PhD, or MD and DDS MRC(Oxon), he may use either or both. If the author has a doctorate, a degree at the master's level is not usually included, although exception may be made when the master's degree represents a different or specialized field (eg, MD, MPH).

Academic degrees below the master's level are omitted. Specialized professional degrees below the master's level (eg, RN, MT (ASCP)) may be used if pertinent. Designations of fellowships or honorary degrees, such as FACP or FACS, are omitted. (Exception is made for authors with degrees obtained in foreign countries.)

Melvin H. Freedman, MD, FRCP (C); E. Fred Saunders, MD, FRCP; James Hilton, MD; Peter D. McClure, CM, MD, FRCP(C)

3.03—When a by-line includes three or more authors with degrees or military titles or both, use semicolons to separate authors' names.

John Smith, PhD, MD; Louis Jones, MD; Nathan S. Grant, PhD

Capt James B. Dane, MC, USA; Lt Col Carl Seller, Jr, MC, USA; Kurt Blount, MD

3.04—Copy such as letters to the editor carries the authors' names at the end of the text rather than as a by-line on the first page. Highest academic or professional degrees (as in **3.02**), institutional affiliation, and city are also given. These are set aligned left, with longest line flush right.

RUPERT B. TURNBULL, JR, MD
Cleveland Clinic Foundation
Cleveland

GERALD A. KAISER, MD
WILLIS H. WILLIAMS, MD
University of Miami School
of Medicine
Miami, Fla

3.05—In by-lines and signatures, military title precedes the author's name; designation of military service follows.

MAJ JOHN McK CATELL, MC, USAF
Aerospace Research Center
Randolph AFB, Tex

3.06—In oriental names, the surname may precede the given name (*Mao* Tse-tung). Follow the author's preference.

CAPITALIZATION—4.00

Words are capitalized sparingly in the scientific publications of the AMA.

4.01—Capitalize proper nouns and most adjectives derived from proper nouns (**4.07**; follow *Webster's International Dictionary*). When a common noun is capitalized in the singular as part of a proper name or in a title (**4.02-4.06**), generally it is not capitalized in the plural.

From the Department of Radiology, University of New Mexico, Albuquerque

From the Departments of Medicine and Pediatrics, University of Tennessee College of Medicine, Memphis.

4.02—Capitalize titles of persons when preceding the name but not when following it, and academic degrees when abbreviated but not when written out. (See also **1.06**.)

Last year, Professor Gelehrte delivered the commencement address; he became professor five years ago.

After dinner, Mayor Richard Hatcher introduced Daniel Walker, governor of Illinois.

Exception: Always capitalize *President* when referring to the President of the United States or of the AMA.

4.03—Capitalize *official titles* of conferences, congresses, postgraduate courses, organizations, institutions, business firms, and governmental agencies, and their departments and other divisions. Do not capitalize *the* (except when part of the official title) or prepositions of three letters or less.

Welfare Council of Metropolitan Chicago

Family Service Association of America

The Johns Hopkins Hospital

The Journal of the American Medical Association

the *New England Journal of Medicine*

the Boy Scouts of America Chicago Lying-In Hospital

Tufts University School of Medicine

Travenol Laboratories, Inc. Pharmaceutical Products Division, Baxter Laboratories, Inc

Supreme Court Congress Department of Labor

House of Representatives Chicago Board of Health

the Third International Congress on Poliomyelitis

the Federation of State Medical Boards in the United States

the Insect Allergy Committee of the American Academy of Allergy

the International Subcommittee on Viral Nomenclature

the Ad Hoc Committee on Evaluation of Experimental Trials

But: an ad hoc committee the federal government congressional the committee

the department the university the company

the association the armed forces federal courts

state representatives the congressman naval service

the board of health the board of trustees

Exceptions:

1. When referring to the AMA, capitalize as follows:

   the Board of Trustees the Board the Association

   the House of Delegates the House

   the Department of Continuing Medical Education the Department

   the Committee on Nursing the Committee

   (*But:* the trustees: the delegates)

2. When the plural of a common noun is part of the title of an organization or institution, it should be capitalized.

   National Institutes of Health

   Hospital for Joint Diseases

   New York Medical College–Flower and Fifth Avenue Hospitals

4.04—Capitalize geographical names, political divisions (except numbered designations), names of specific locations, and accepted designations for regions. Do not capitalize expressions indicating general directions or location. (See also **4.07**; follow *Webster's*.)

Mississippi River Atlantic Ocean the Great Lakes

(*But:* Mississippi and Missouri rivers; Atlantic and Pacific oceans)

North Pole British Isles United Kingdom

Straits of Gibraltar Isle of Wight the Orient

New Trier Township Cook County

New York City Mexico City

(*But:* Quebec city) the Bad Lands the Iron Curtain the Loop (Chicago)

(*But:* the fifth precinct: the 23rd congressional district)

She lives in the Far East, in central China. Her home is east of Chungking but not as far east as Wuhan.

He is a Westerner. He lives in the West, 15 miles west of Salt Lake City.

CAPITALIZATION

4.05—Capitalize proper names of languages, people, races, political parties, religions, and religious denominations and sects. Do not capitalize the common nouns following these designations. Do not capitalize political doctrines. Do not capitalize *white* or *black* as designation of race.

the English language   Sanskrit   Hebrew

Orientals   Europeans   Mohawks   of Spanish ancestry

Protestant   Catholic   Jew   Muslim   Christian

a Baptist church   (*But:* First Baptist Church)

He is a member of the Republican party, and his brother is a Democrat. Both endorse the principles of democracy in our republican form of government. Both are democratic in their attitudes toward social equality.

4.06—Capitalize names of historical events, treaties, official names of adopted laws and bills, and specific parts of adopted laws and bills. Do not capitalize common nouns and adjectives in proposed laws, bills, or amendments that have not been passed.

Battle of Gettysburg   Geneva Convention   World War II

Louisiana Purchase   Social Security Act   Bill of Rights

Civil Rights Law   Fifth Amendment   Public Law 89-74

Medicare   Medicare Act   Title XVIII

(*But:* King-Anderson bill; Medicare law; premarital laws)

4.07—For capitalization of words derived from proper nouns, follow the bold-face listings in the most recent edition of *Webster's* for nonmedical terms; follow *Dorland's* and *Stedman's* for medical terms. (See also **10.4/4).**

Do not capitalize the following:

addisonism   fallopian   parkinsonism

anglicize   freudian   pasteurize

bohemian   mendelian   platonic

cesarean   mongoloid   roentgenogram

4.08—When an eponym is included in the name of a disease, syndrome, sign, position, or similar designation, capitalize the eponym but not the common noun. Eponyms do not take the possessive form. Consult *Current*

Medical Information and Terminology, Dorland's, and *Stedman's*. (See also **10.04/3.**)

Raynaud disease	Trendelenburg position
Marfan syndrome	Babinski sign
Hodgkin disease	Sippy diet Gram stain

4.09—Capitalize major words in titles and subtitles of publications, parts of publications, musical compositions, plays (stage and screen), radio and television programs, and names of ships and airplanes. (See also **14.12/13, 20.02/1.**)

Do not capitalize a conjunction, article, or preposition of less than four letters, except when it is the first or last word in a title or subtitle. *Do* capitalize a two-letter verb.

What Is Sarcoma?

4.10—In listed references, follow **15.10-15.12** for capitalization of titles and subtitles of articles, parts of books, bulletins, and pamphlets, in English or in a foreign language.

4.11—Capitalize major words in table heads, centerheads, and sideheads, as in **4.09.**

4.12—In titles, subtitles, table heads, centerheads, and sideheads, do not capitalize the second part of a hyphenated compound if (1) either part is a hyphenated prefix or suffix, or (2) both parts together constitute a single word. (See also **14.08.**)

Urticaria-like	Re-treat	Self-Preservation
Follow-up Studies	X-ray	Drug-Resistant
Tumor-like Changes	Intra-arterial Embolism	
Vaso-occlusive Disease	Anti-infective Drugs	

4.13—After a colon, capitalize the first word (1) in references and (2) in the text when the following enumeration or explanation contains two or more complete sentences. (See also **14.03/2.**)

4.14—For capitalization in quoted material, follow the quotation exactly. When the structure suggests use of a capital at the start of a quoted statement, a lowercase letter may be capitalized.

As stated in the report, "A candidate may be admitted if he has completed two years of medical school."

(*But:* The report noted that "a candidate may be admitted . . .")

CAPITALIZATION

4.15—Capitalize trademarks and proprietary names of drugs and brand names of manufactured products and equipment, except for a few oddities like pHisoHex. Do not capitalize generic names or descriptive terms. (See also **10.05/3, 10.06/1.**)

> A Dacron implant was used.

4.16—Capitalize the name of a genus when used in the singular, with or without a species name. Do not capitalize when used in the plural or adjectivally. Do not capitalize the name of a species, variety, or subspecies. Do capitalize class, order, family, or tribe. (See also **10.07/1-10.07/5.**)

4.17—For capitalization of virus names, see **10.12.**

4.18—Do not capitalize names of seasons.

> winter   spring   summer   fall   autumn

4.19—Capitalize personifications and designations of deity.

> the Almighty   Mother Nature   God
>
> Mother Earth   Allah

4.20—Capitalize recognized holidays and holy days.

> Easter   Passover   Fourth of July   St Patrick's Day
>
> Holy Week   Thanksgiving Day   Christmas Eve

4.21—When used as specific designations, with or without numerals, capitalize *Table, Figure,* and *Fig.*

> as shown in the Table
>
> as seen in compact bundles (Figure)
>
> summarized in Table 2
>
> as given in Fig 2 through 7
>
> cultures yielded *Candida* (Fig 3)

4.22—Do not capitalize the following words, even when used as specific designations:

case	experiment	grant
chapter	factor	group
chromosome	fraction	lead
column	grade	method

note	patient	stage
page	phase	type
paragraph	section	volume
part	series	wave

CORRECT USAGE—5.00

Although the whole stylebook is a guide to "correct usage," this special section is included to specify correct forms and use of terms or to highlight difficulties involving solecisms, jargon, vulgarisms, barbarisms, colloquialisms, neologisms, malapropisms, and misused and abused terms in copy written for or by persons in the medical field.

For accepted medical terminology consult the most recent editions of *Dorland's Illustrated Medical Dictionary, Stedman's Medical Dictionary,* and additional authoritative sources as follows: *Current Medical Information and Terminology; Current Procedural Terminology; AMA Drug Evaluations; Bergey's Manual of Determinative Bacteriology;* Dubos and Hirsch: *Bacterial and Mycotic Infections of Man; US Pharmacopeia, Merck Index;* McKusick and Claiborne: *Medical Genetics;* and *Gradwohl's Clinical Laboratory Methods and Diagnosis.*

For accepted nonmedical terminology, consult the *current* edition of *Webster's International Dictionary. Webster's New Collegiate* and *American Heritage Dictionary* may also be used. In the current editions, *Webster's* does not differentiate proper from improper uses of words, but the *American Heritage Dictionary* does. Use American spelling rather than British, except in proper names, titles, and direct quotations. When two spellings are listed in *Webster's,* use the first if they are separated by *also;* use either if they are separated by *or,* except when one is not the American spelling. (*Cigarette* is preferred to *cigaret; formulas or formulae* may be used.)

5.01—**Eponyms**—Use the latest edition of *Current Medical Information and Terminology* as a guide for proper usage of eponyms. If an author uses an eponym that is an unpreferred term, the eponym may be given in parentheses after the preferred term. Eponyms are not written in the possessive form.

Wilms tumor	Hodgkin disease
Graves disease	Ewing sarcoma

5.02—**Misused Terms**—A number of commonly misused or confused terms are listed here and the correct usage indicated.

acute, chronic—Generally, these terms should be reserved for description of symptoms, conditions, or diseases.

The unit contained 20 patients undergoing long-term hemodialysis.

age, aged—The adjective, *aged*, not the noun, *age*, should be used to describe a person with respect to age.

The patient, aged 45 years, weighed exactly 50 kg.

aggravate, irritate—When *an existing condition* is made worse, it is "aggravated." When tissue is caused to be inflamed or sore, it is "irritated."

apt, likely, liable—*Apt* implies a habitual tendency or volition; *likely* merely implies probability; *liable* implies the possibility of risk or disadvantage to the subject.

The patient's mother is likely to visit him.

The child is apt to stammer when he is excited.

Jaywalkers are liable to be run over (killed).

The patient is apt to be hungry.

The patient will likely die.

Patients who receive immunosuppressant drugs are liable to get fungal infections.

biopsy—The noun "biopsy" means the procedure of removing and examining tissue, cells, or fluids from the living body. The word is not to be used as a verb. Observations are made on the biopsy specimen, not on the biopsy itself.

Incorrect	*Correct*
The mass was biopsied.	A biopsy of the mass was done.
Biopsy was negative.	Results of the biopsy were normal.
The biopsy showed fibrosis.	The biopsy specimen showed fibrosis.

case, patient—A case is a particular instance of disease. A patient is a person who is under medical care. A case is evaluated and reported. A patient is admitted to the hospital, examined, given medication, discharged.

Roentgenograms were obtained in all cases.

This report describes a patient with undiagnosed acromegaly. Five cases of acromegaly were treated in our clinic within the last two years.

compare to vs compare with—Most often, one thing should be compared *with* another. To "compare to" is to show how something of one order resembles that of another: "She was compared to the moon."

compose, comprise, consist—These words are not synonymous. *Comprise* means "to consist of," "to be composed of." The whole comprises the parts; the parts do not comprise the whole. (Avoid "to be comprised of.")

A hearty soup is composed of many ingredients.

A hearty soup comprises many ingredients.

A hearty soup comprises (consists of) liquid, vegetables, and meat or seafood.

The art of soup-making consists in achieving the proper balance of many ingredients.

deliver, delivery—An infant is delivered; a woman is *delivered of* an infant. Popular reference to "health care *delivery*" is inappropriate; care (treatment, examination, counsel of patients) is *given* or *provided*, not delivered.

Problems in health care provision are of national concern.

develop—Despite the increasing use of this verb in the transitive sense, it is jargon to state that "the patient developed a disease." Rather, the correct form is "the disease developed."

A thrombus developed in the femoral artery.
The patient's condition did not improve and anxiety developed.

diagnose, identify—A patient is neither diagnosed nor identified (unless his identity is actually in question). A condition or disease is *diagnosed*. A pathogen is *identified*.

die of, die from—Persons die *of*, not *from* specific diseases.

diurese is not an acceptable verb.

The patient was given diuretics.
Diuresis was instituted for the next 12 hours.

doctor, physician—Generally, "doctor" should be changed to "physician" when the latter is meant specifically.

document, report—An author who states that he is "documenting" his findings, observations, or study details should in fact be "providing factual or substantial support by documents or other evidence for statements made or hypothesis proposed." Often, he is not documenting his data but merely *reporting* them. However, if the author is substantiating a diagnosis by objective findings from the patient's record, he is documenting it. It is recommended that the word document have an absolute meaning. The use of qualifiers weakens the meaning. *Poorly documented* should be replaced by *not documented.*

> To our knowledge, this is the first documented report of postprandial hypertension.

> We studied 46 cases and report [not document] the outcomes for 42.

dose, dosage—A dose is the quantity to be administered at one time or the total quantity administered. Dosage is the regulated administration of doses, and is usually expressed in terms of a quantity per unit of time.

> The patient received an initial dose of 50 mg and thereafter dosage of 25 mg three times a day until he had received a total dose of 500 mg.

due to, owing to—Although the distinction between the adjectival and adverbial forms is becoming increasingly blurred, we prefer to keep the distinction. Use it only as a predicate adjective following a linking verb.

> His hesitancy was *due to* (adjective) fear.
> He hesitated *owing to* (adverb) fear.

etiology—Do not use it as a synonym for cause. *Etiology* encompasses all the possible causes of a disease.

> The etiology of cancer is a maze of unknowns.

> The cause of the pain was an occult lesion.

etc—Use *etc* with discretion. It should *never* be used as the last item in an inclusive list or as a catch-all for an incomplete list whose components are not self-evident (a "lazy etc"). However, it may be used in a noninclusive listing when a complete list would be unwieldy *and* its content is obvious to the reader.

> *Wrong:* A first aid kit should include aspirin, emetics, self-adhesive bandages, etc.

> *Right:* Cough arising from irritation of pharyngeal mucosa can be managed with demulcents and sialagogues (hard candy, cough drops, etc).

Do not use *etc* when the listing is preceded by such wording as *ie*, *eg*, or *for example.*

Use a comma before *etc* when it is preceded by more than one term but not when preceded by one term only.

evaluate—Patients are not evaluated; conditions and diseases are.

fever, temperature—Fever is a rise of body temperature above normal. If a patient has a temperature of 37.8 C, he has a fever of 0.8 C. The following form is also correct: The patient was febrile (37.8 C).

follow, observe—A case is followed. A patient is observed. Either a case or a patient may be followed up.

-ic, -ical—*Webster's*, *Stedman's*, and *Dorland's* dictionaries are resources for deciding the appropriate suffix form for given adjectives. Note that the "-ical" form is more remote from the word root and may have a meaning refined beyond that of the "-ic" form. Although "elliptic" may be used in the same sense as "elliptical," the latter is preferred as the adjective form. The important guideline is that use of terms be consistent throughout an article. Usually, the "-al" may be omitted unless its absence changes the meaning of the word, such as logic-logical, physic-physical.

imply, infer—To imply is to suggest, to indicate or express indirectly. To infer is to conclude, to draw conclusions from.

His statement implies that he is happy, but from his sullen manner I infer that he is still discontent.

individual, person—In most instances, the noun "individual" should be changed to "person," unless the meaning of distinction from class or group must be retained.

infect, infest—Endoparasites (those that live within the host's body) *infect* or produce an *infection*. Ectoparasites (those that are attached to the skin or temporarily invade the superficial tissues of the host) *infest* or produce an *infestation*. For example:

The *infection* was caused by *Salmonella enteritidis*.

The patient was *infested* with lice.

The boy had a hookworm infection.

marked, markedly—When these terms are overused, appropriate alternatives should be used to avoid monotony.

Not preferred	*Preferred*
His condition was markedly improved.	His condition was greatly improved.
A marked contrast was noted.	A sharp contrast was noted.

militate, mitigate—These two words are often confused; they are not synonymous. *Militate* means to have force as evidence; it "derives from the same source as *military*, which has to do with soldiery and fighting, and is used especially with *against"* (*JAMA* 213:290, 1970). To *mitigate* is to moderate, abate, soften.

The leukocytosis militates against that diagnosis.

The cold packs did much to mitigate the patient's discomfort.

necessitate, require—These terms are not synonymous; *necessitate* means "to make necessary," and *require* means to "have a need for." A patient may require treatment, but the treatment would *necessitate* (not *require*) specific tests, equipment, applications.

negative, normal—Examinations and most laboratory tests are neither negative nor normal. The observations, results, or findings from examinations and tests are normal or abnormal. Cultures, tests for microorganisms, tests for specific reactions, and reactions to tests may be negative or positive.

Results of physical examination were normal.

Physical examination showed no abnormalities.

Findings from laboratory tests were normal.

Laboratory tests showed normal values.

Wassermann reaction was negative.

A tuberculin patch test was positive.

Cultures were negative for *Clostridium botulinum*.

Electroencephalograms, electrocardiograms, isotope scans, and roentgenograms are "pictures" and are, therefore, normal or abnormal, not negative or positive.

operate, operate on—A surgeon does not operate a patient.

A surgeon operates on a patient.

He may do an exploratory operation.

over, more than—In some constructions, "over" may be ambiguous when "more than" is meant. In such cases, "more than" is preferred to "over."

Ambiguous: The cases were followed up over two years.

Correct: The cases were followed up for more than two years.

Correct: The cases were followed up for a period of two years.

paramedic—Because the terms "paramedic" or "paramedics" are vague, more specific terms are preferred. "Physician's assistant," "allied health personnel," or appropriate professional titles ("nurse," "anesthetist") should usually be substituted.

parameter—"Parameter" is much overused (like the term "significant"). It has a specific meaning in a statistical sense and should not be used simply to mean measurement, value, or number. Ordinarily, except when a descriptive quantity for a statistical population is meant, "parameter" should be changed to read "measurement," "value," "quantity," "variable," "number," or comparable terms.

people, persons—In a specific sense, "people" means "an aggregate of persons." Stating "two people died" is therefore less correct than saying "two persons died."

patient is often used to mean *person*. A sick person not receiving medical attention is not a patient; there is no such thing as "untreated patients" or "normal patients" in the population.

preponderant, predominant—When "having greater prevalence" is meant, use *preponderant*. When "having superior strength, influence, or authority" is intended, use *predominant*.

prevalence, incidence—These words are not synonymous. *Prevalence* is the quality or state of being widespread, common, or prevailing, or the degree to which something is prevalent. *Incidence* is simply the rate of occurrence per unit of time or per unit of population.

The prevalence of influenza in the winter of 1970 increased; the incidence rose from 20 to 40/1,000 population.

regime, regimen—*Regime* is a system of management of government; an administration. When a system of therapy is meant, *regimen* is the correct term.

The regimen included isosorbide dinitrate, 5 mg/day.

reveal—The term "reveal" is overused, and so should be avoided, but it may be used occasionally to relieve monotony of expression.

roentgen, x-ray, roentgenogram, radiograph—A roentgen is a unit of x-radiation. An x-ray is a roentgen ray. A roentgenogram is an image made by means of roentgen rays. A radiograph is a record or photograph made by radioactivity: it refers only to scans. Never use "radiogram" unless it means a message sent by radio waves. Do not use *x-ray* as a synonym for roentgenogram. If an alternate term is needed, use *x-ray film* or simply *film*. Do not use *radiography* as synonym for *roentgenography*, nor *radiograph* for *roentgenogram*. *Radiology* and *roentgenology* are synonymous.

significant(ly)—When an author uses "significant" (or "significance") where it might be confused with its strict statistical meaning, it should be changed to a specific term such as "important" (or "importance"), "substantial" (or "substantive"), "notable," "great"; when statistical significance is meant, *P* values are usually given.

suspicious of, suggestive of—To be *suspicious of* is to be distrustful of. To be *suggestive of* is to give a suggestion or indication of.

The patient's symptoms are suggestive of measles.

The physician is suspicious of a hasty diagnosis.

that, which—*That* is preferred to introduce restrictive clauses; *which* is used to introduce nonrestrictive clauses. Restrictive clauses are essential to the meaning of the sentence and are not set off by commas. Nonrestrictive clauses can be omitted without changing the meaning of the sentence and are set off.

The organization that supports the bill will benefit from it.
(The organization is identified by the restrictive clause.)

The organization, which supports the bill, will benefit from it.
(More information is given in the nonrestrictive clause about the previously identified organization.)

toxic, toxicity—*Toxic* means "pertaining to or caused by poison or toxin; poisonous." *Toxicity* is the quality, state, or degree of being poisonous. A patient is *not* toxic. A patient does *not* have toxicity.

Carmustine is a very toxic drug.

A drug has a toxic effect on a patient.

A patient is in a toxic condition.

The toxicity of the drug must be considered.

(*But:* A patient has a toxic reaction. A drug is toxic to a patient.)

utilize, use—Because "utilize" is a term that "may suggest the discovery of a new, profitable, or practical use for something," it should be replaced by the word "use" when the general meaning is intended. Generally, "use" is the intended term.

5.03—**Redundancies**—A redundancy is a term that uses more words than are necessary. Here are common redundancies to avoid (*redundant words are italicized*):

consensus *of opinion*   fuse *together*

orange *in color*   large *in size*

mortality *rate*	period *of time*
lenticular *in character*	tender *to the touch*
two halves	*quite* complete
soft *in consistency*	round *in shape*
in order to	rough *in texture*
sour-*tasting*	(was) *a* loud *sound*
(was) *a* pungent *odor*	

5.04—**Contractions**—Do not use contractions, except as given in a direct quotation or in articles in an informal or colloquial style.

5.05—**Medicalese and Jargon**—Words or phrases that are peculiar to conversations among medical personnel and are generally inappropriate in scientific writing. Examples of expressions and their corrected forms are given here.

Jargon	Correct Form
4+ albuminuria	proteinuria (4+) *or* urine reaction for protein was 4+
blood sugar	blood glucose [query the author]
cardiac diet	diet for patients with cardiac disease
clinical material (meaning patients)	patients in the study
congenital heart	congenital heart disease, defect
cytology was normal	cytologic findings were normal
hyperglycemia of 150 mg	hyperglycemia (150 mg/100 ml)
left heart failure	left ventricular failure [query the author]
leukocytosis of 15,000	leukocytosis (15,000/cu mm) *or* a leukocyte count of 15,000/cu mm
No pathology was found.	No pathologic condition was found.
prepped	prepared
psychiatric floor	psychiatric ward, department, service

right hemothorax	right-sided hemothorax *or* hemothorax on the right
serology was negative	serologic findings were normal
severe symptomatology	severe symptoms
skull series	skull roentgenographic series
urinary infection	urinary tract infection *or* infection of the urinary tract
upper respiratory infection	upper respiratory tract infection
jugular ligation	jugular vein ligation *or* ligation of the jugular vein

Avoid the following expressions when possible without cumbersome rephrasing or verbosity:

Patients on, placed on, started on, discharged on a drug (eg, chloramphenicol).

> *Avoid:* For patients on chloramphenicol. . . .
> The patient was started (placed) on chloramphenicol.
> The patient was discharged on chloramphenicol.

> *Preferred:* For patients receiving chloramphenicol. . . .
> Chloramphenicol therapy was started.
> The patient was discharged on a regimen of chloramphenicol.

Intravenous, oral, parenteral, topical, or rectal drugs—In describing drugs, these are acceptable terms when these are the usual or intended routes of administration. Generally, however, drugs are neither systemic or local but are given for systemic or local effect.

Some topical ointments produce systemic effects.

Parenteral penicillin is often preferred to oral penicillin.

Intravenously injected heroin is often severely contaminated.

5.06—The following terms should be changed to preferred forms:

Avoid	*Use*
Caucasian	white
colored (meaning Negro)	black
doctor	physician

double-blindfold study	double-blind study
expired, succumbed	died
male, female (as nouns)	man, woman, boy, girl
mortality rate	death rate or mortality
osteopath, osteopathy	osteopathic physician, osteopathic medicine
over (meaning in excess of)	more than
sacrificed	killed
therapy of (a disease or condition)	therapy for
treatment for (a disease or condition)	treatment of

In addition, appropriate terms should be substituted for the following hackneyed or unfelicitous terms and expressions: *armamentarium*, *paucity*, *initiate*, *examination revealed*, *experienced a weight loss* (use *lost weight*), *presented with* (use *had* in most instances), *received no therapy*.

Colloquialisms and vulgarisms should be avoided in scientific writing; however, occasionally, exceptions may be made in editorials, informal articles, or the like.

5.07—**Age, Sex Referents**—*Infants* are persons from birth to 2 years of age (24 months).

Children are persons from age 2 to 13 years. Sometimes, *children* may be used more broadly to encompass persons from birth to 13 years of age. They should be referred to as boys or girls.

Adolescents are persons from 13 to 17 years of age. They may also be referred to as teen-agers or as boys or girls.

Adults are persons 18 years of age or older and should be referred to as *men* or *women*.

5.07—Whenever possible, a patient should be identified as a "man," "woman," "boy," "girl," or "infant," not as "a male" or "a female." Occasionally, however, a study group may comprise children and adults of both sexes. Then, use of *male* or *female* as adjectives is appropriate.

The control group included 77 male and 83 female subjects [male subjects including both men and boys, female subjects including both women and girls].

5.08—**Body Parts**—Authors often err in referring to such things as the "right heart," "left colon," "upper arm," and "left neck." Generally, these terms can be corrected by insertion of a phrase such as "part of the" or "side of the," as noted in these examples:

the right side of the heart

left side of the chest or left hemithorax

(*But:* proximal jejunum and distal esophagus)

The *upper extremity* comprises the arm (extending from the shoulder to the elbow), the *forearm* (from elbow to wrist), and the *hand*. The *lower extremity* comprises the *thigh* (extending from the hip to the knee), the *leg* (from the knee to the ankle), and the *foot*. Therefore, references to upper arm, lower arm, upper/lower leg are inappropriate and often ambiguous. In such a case, the author should be queried.

5.09—**Clock referents**—Occasionally, reference to a locus of insertion, position, or attitude is given in terms of a clock-face orientation, whether in a vertical or horizontal plane, as seen by the viewer. Avoid ambiguity by indicating orientation and by mentioning the word "position."

Avoid: The needle was inserted into the left eye at 9 o'clock.
Use: The needle was inserted into the left eye at the 9-o'clock position, facing the patient.

NB—The terms "clockwise" and "counterclockwise" can be also misleading. The plane of reference should be specified in the event of ambiguity.

5.10—**Race**—Reference to race should be deleted from reports of cases unless the information is essential to the data for the disease entities involved (eg, sickle cell disorders in black patients, paragonimiasis in Orientals, Tay-Sachs disease in Jews). If, in the opinion of the author, information about race is essential, it should be given. (See also **4.05.**)

5.11—**Values**—Usually, in reports of clinical or laboratory data, the substance per se is not reported; rather, a value is given that was obtained by measurement of a substance or some function or constituent of it. For example, one does not report "blood" but rather blood pressure, blood cell count, bleeding time. Some other correct forms are as follows:

differential cell **count**

hemoglobin **level**

agglutination **titer** (a ratio)

protein-bound iodine (PBI) **level**

prothrombin **time**

pulse **rate** (beats per minute)

respirations

sedimentation **rate**

total serum cholesterol **value**

rise in antibody **activity**

creatinine **level** or **clearance**

serum phosphorus **concentration**

rise in bilirubin **level** or **increase** in bilirubin

In reports of findings from clinical examination or laboratory studies, data may be enumerated without repeating *value*, *level*, etc, in accordance with the following example:

Laboratory studies disclosed the following values: hemoglobin, 8.5 gm/100 ml; hematocrit, 29%; WBC, 18,400/cu mm, with 83% neutrophils, 12% lymphocytes, and 5% monocytes; blood glucose, 116 mg/100 ml; serum uric acid, 4.0 mg/100; cephalin flocculation, 0 in 48 hours; and serum alkaline phosphatase, 14.8 King-Armstrong units/100 ml.

5.12—**Articles**—The article *a* is used before words or abbreviations beginning with a sounded consonant; *an* is used before those beginning with a sounded vowel.

a dog (*d* sound)
a WCTU poster (*d* sound)
a hematocrit (*h* sound)
a UHF station (*y* sound)

an ultraviolet source (*a* sound)
an honor (*o* sound)
an HMO plan (*a* sound)
an MS degree (*e* sound)

5.13—**Grammar**—The following are common errors.
Danglers—A modifying word or phrase must refer clearly to the word modified. Violation of this rule often results in nonsense. Be especially wary of misplaced participial and prepositional phrases.

Nonsense: On May 16, the patient was first seen by the referring physician in a severely debilitated condition.
Sense: When first seen by the referring physician on May 16, the patient was in a severely debilitated condition.

Nonsense: A left posterolateral thoracotomy was performed under general anesthesia.
Sense: With the patient under general anesthesia, a left posterolateral thoracotomy was performed.

Nonsense: Having a distended bladder, one of us catheterized the patient.
Sense: Because the patient had a distended bladder, one of us catheterized the patient.

Nonsense: Compared with *Salmonella* organisms, Jones and Turner reported a greater average organism size.
Sense: Jones and Turner reported a greater average organism size, as compared with *Salmonella* organisms.

Faulty Constructions—Nonsense may also result from other illogical arrangements of sentence elements, misplacement of modifiers, or absence of otherwise presumed-to-be-present subjects. Here are some examples:

When first seen on Jan 29, the patient complained of abdominal pain for three weeks.

Chronic lymphocytic leukemia showed the longest survival time.

Almost every patient was followed to death or to January 1971.

With the knees flexed and drawn up toward the abdomen and the upper extremities held in flexion, a not infrequent occurrence, the physician may find caring for the patient a problem.

Tense—The past perfect tense is used for events that were begun and completed in the past.

Five years ago, the patient had undergone a herniorraphy.

Present tense

Our data demonstrate this relationship.

I believe that the two events are unrelated.

Apparently, radical mastectomy is the treatment of choice among US surgeons.

Past tense

Smith et al reported 15 cases of acromegaly.

We treated 17 schizophrenic patients.

5.14—**Expendable Words**—These terms can often be omitted without affecting the meaning, and often improve the readability and comprehensibility, of a sentence:

quite   very   it is important to note that

needless to say

NB—For the correct use of *etc* refer to **5.02.**

FOOTNOTES/ANNOTATIONS—6.00

Although a "footnote" provides subordinately related information at the foot of a column, the term "footnotes" has come to mean all supplementary information pertinent to an article. Hence, acknowledgments appearing at the end of the text and not at the foot of a column are nonetheless called "footnotes." (See References, **15.00.**)

Note: Footnotes within the text should be avoided. Explanatory material can usually be incorporated parenthetically into the text.

6.01—**Order of Footnotes**—The preferred order for first-page footnotes, as applicable, is as follows: acceptance (and/or receipt), affiliations, death of author (dagger), "read before," disclaimer, reprint address.

6.02—**Acceptance (Receipt) of Manuscript**—Footnotes showing dates of submission, receipt, or acceptance of articles vary among the specialty journals and are excluded from *JAMA.* Follow these examples, as applicable:

Submitted for publication May 4, 1975.

Accepted for publication Oct 5, 1975.

Received for publication May 3, 1975; accepted Nov 17.

Submitted for publication Oct 29, 1974; accepted Jan 10, 1975.

6.03—**Affiliations**—The institutions with which an author is professionally affiliated are given in a footnote. The footnote does not indicate the author's title or rank at such an institution. The city in which a hospital, university, or organization is located should be included.

Wording should be concise, in the style indicated in the following examples. For abbreviation and capitalization of titles and names of departments and organizations, follow specific rules (**1.01, 1.06, 1.09, 4.02, 4.03**).

From the Department of Medicine, Northwestern University Medical School, Chicago.

From the Departments of Surgery (Dr Doe) and Medicine (Dr Roe), University of Kentucky School of Medicine, Lexington.

From Memorial Hospital of DuPage County, Elmhurst, Ill (Dr Jay), and Children's Memorial Hospital, Chicago (Dr Kay).

Dr Piedicue is in private practice.

If an author has moved since doing the work reported, his present location should be given. If an author is a fellow doing research sponsored by an organization, this may be included in the first-page footnote.

From the Connaught Medical Research Laboratories, Toronto. Dr Glore is now with the University of British Columbia, Vancouver.

From the Argonne Cancer Research Hospital, Chicago. Dr Blank is a fellow of the American Cancer Society.

6.04—**Death**—If an author has died before his article is published, a dagger (†) should follow his name in the by-line, and one of the following footnotes should be inserted after the affiliation footnote.

†Dr Bland died Oct 17, 1973.   †Deceased.

6.05—**"Read before"**—The following forms are used for material that has been read before a society meeting.

Read in part before the Medical Society of the District of Columbia, Washington, Oct 10, 1973.

Adapted from a chairman's address read before the Section on Internal Medicine at the 123rd annual convention of the American Medical Association, Chicago, June 23, 1974.

Presented as a scientific exhibit at the 118th annual convention of the American Medical Association, New York, June 13-17, 1969.

Presented as the Abraham Jacobi Award Address at the 123rd annual convention of the American Medical Association, Chicago, June 22, 1974.

6.06—**Disclaimer**—A footnote of disclaimer is used only when provided by the author. This notation precedes the reprint address. Use the author's phrasing.

The views expressed herein are those of the authors and do not necessarily reflect the views of the US Air Force or the Department of Defense.

6.07—**Reprint Address**—The address of the author or of one of the authors is given in a footnote, for readers who wish to request reprints or additional information. If possible, this should be a complete address, including the name of the hospital or university, number, and street, and should include the US Post Office postal codes (eg, AZ for Arizona, IL for Illinois), and zip code number. Use the forms given in the following examples. Observe specific rules for punctuation and abbreviation in addresses. Note that this address always ends with a period.

Reprint requests to St Francis Hospital, 355 Ridge Ave, Evanston, IL 60202 (Dr D'Assisi).

To distinguish between authors with the same last name, use first initial or, if necessary, full name.

Address of a person not included in the by-line:
Reprint requests to the Bridge Defense Foundation, 111 N First St, French Lick, IN 47432 (Barry M. Horatio, MD).

6.08—**Acknowledgments**—Acknowledgments are made in unnumbered footnotes at the end of the communication, with acknowledgment of financial support preceding others.

Wording should be formal, concise, and specific. Omit such phrases as "kind generosity of," "who greatly aided," "express our gratitude," and "through the courtesy of."

Acknowledgment should also be made of material that has been printed elsewhere. The author must have permission from the previous publisher for the use of such material and should be queried if he does not indicate that it has been obtained. (See also **8.07, 8.12.**)

This investigation was supported by Public Health Service research grant 5-TI-MH-8654-09 from the National Institute of Mental Health.

This investigation was supported by the Russek Foundation, Inc, Staten Island, NY.

This investigation was supported by a grant in memory of Dorothy V. Murry.

Figures 2, 3, and 5 are reproduced with permission from the *New England Journal of Medicine* (98:546-601, 1974).

Figure 6 is reproduced with permission from Osmotherly.[9]

Figures are reproduced with permission of Ford's Theater Museum, National Park Service, Washington, DC.

Alfred G. Cane, MD, gave permission to report case 5.

Acknowledgment of grants from federal agencies should include the grant number. Request the number from the author if he has not supplied it. Other grant numbers are not required but may be included if supplied.

For the correct names of pharmaceutical companies, see the current *AMA Drug Evaluations*. Use abbreviations as specified in **1.08.** Include the name of the city in which the firm is located (**1.12**).

Postmortem studies were done by James B. Janus, MD.

Robert R. Crown, MD, supplied the electrocardiographic interpretations in cases 2 and 6.

The procainamide hydrochloride used in this investigation was supplied as Pronestyl Hydrochloride through Jonas M. Brown, MD, of E. R. Squibb & Sons, Division of Olin Mathieson Chemical Corp, New York.

The recorder used in this study was a Polyviso Recorder, model 67-1200, provided by Sanborn Co, Cambridge, Mass.

Grace Yang, MS, assisted in the electron microscopic studies; Ann Bretschneider and Frances Clark provided technical assistance in the histology laboratory.

GREEK LETTERS—7.00

7.01—Greek letters in copy should be marked for the typesetter's attention by writing, in the margin, the letters "Gk" followed by the code numbers in the following list.

1	A	Alpha	13	N	Nu	26	β	beta	39	o	omicron
2	B	Beta	14	Ξ	Xi	27	γ	gamma	40	π	pi
3	Γ	Gamma	15	O	Omicron	28	δ	delta	41	ρ	rho
4	Δ	Delta	16	Π	Pi	29	ϵ	epsilon	42	σ	sigma
5	E	Epsilon	17	P	Rho	30	ζ	zeta-	43	ς	sigma
6	Z	Zeta	18	Σ	Sigma	31	η	eta	44	τ	tau
7	H	Eta	19	T	Tau	32	θ	theta	45	υ	upsilon
8	Θ	Theta	20	Y	Upsilon	33	ι	iota	46	φ	phi
8a	Θ	Theta	21	Φ	Phi	34	κ	kappa	46a	ϕ	phi
9	I	Iota	22	X	Chi	35	λ	lambda	47	χ	chi
10	K	Kappa	23	Ψ	Psi	36	μ	mu	48	ψ	psi
11	Λ	Lambda	24	Ω	Omega	37	ν	nu	49	ω	omega
12	M	Mu	25	α	alpha	38	ξ	xi	50	ϑ	theta

Common uses of Greek letters include these terms:

γ-globulin κ light chain Δ^9-tetrahydrocannabinol

ΔT β-adrenergic β-hemolytic

7.02—**Statistics**—Greek letters are frequently used in statistical formulas and notations. (See also **17.00.**)

Σ (summation)

β-level (expected proportion of type II errors)

ϵ^2 (epsilon-square, differentiation ratio without bias)

η (eta, correlation ratio)

σ (sigma, standard deviation)

σ^2 (sigma-square, variance)

χ^2 (chi-square, measure of discrepancy between two frequency distributions) (To avoid confusion with capital X, always specify Greek 47)

χ^2_r (chi-square sub-r, Friedman statistic)

ρ (rho, correlation)

7.03—**Titles, Subtitles (Including Sideheads and Centerheads)**—Use the Greek letter (eg, β) rather than the spelled out word (eg, beta) in titles and subtitles. Do not capitalize the Greek letter.

The first non-Greek letter following the Greek letter should be capitalized.

β-Carotene and Sunlight

α-Fetoprotein in Viral Hepatitis

7.04—**Drugs, Chemical Terms**—For some generic terms, use of Greek letters is optional. Ordinarily, when the Greek prefix is separated from the specific term, that prefix should be given as the letter (eg, β) and not written out. For chemical terms, use of Greek letters is almost always preferred.

α-tocopherol	β-amylase
β-lactose	α-naphthol

N,N-dimenthyl-γ-phenylcyclohexanepropylamine

(*But:* betamethasone acetate)

NB—Proprietary names should be used in their "official" form; names in which the Greek term is not separated from the other elements by a hyphen should retain the form given in the *AMA Drug Evaluations*.

For definitive information on correct usage, consult the AMA Department of Drugs.

7.05—**Beginning a Sentence**—When a sentence begins with a Greek letter, retain the Greek letter and capitalize the first non-Greek letter.

β-Hemolytic streptococci were identified.

8.01—A legend must accompany each illustration other than clearly labeled structural formulas of chemical compounds. Occasionally, special circumstances may dictate that figures have a numerical designation only. In such cases, the word "Figure" is spelled out.

Figure 1. Figure 2.

8.02—Legends should be brief, each stating clearly and concisely what the figure shows. In general, a legend should be set flush left and begin with a noun clause, followed by a period. Often, this will suffice. If more information is needed, it should be given in sentence form. Omit unnecessary words, such as "photograph of," or "graph showing."

Whenever possible, omit the articles *a, an,* and *the.* Detailed explanations should be deleted from legends and incorporated into the text.

Fig 3.—Eosinophilic inclusion (arrow) in greatly enlarged oligodendroglial nucleus. Typical Cowdry type A inclusions were not found (hematoxylin-eosin, ×350).

When there is only one illustration, omit numerical designation.

Acute conjunctivitis with profuse purulent discharge.

8.03—**Reference to Areas and Parts of a Figure**—To refer to an area of a single illustration, use phrases such as "at left," "at right," "at center," etc.

Fig 5.—Pelvis of patient with mild epiphysiolysis. Note "beaking" of inferior edge of capital epiphysis at left.

In a figure consisting of two or more separate illustrations (parts), use a single legend. Identify the parts as left, right, top, bottom, or center, rather than by letter designations. Capitalize location when used at the beginning of a sentence or independent clause (and capitalize the first word following the designation); lowercase and enclose in parentheses when parts are indicated within a sentence or phrase. When a figure has many parts or they are not symmetrically arranged, letters may be used for easier identification.

Fig 1.—Transfemoral arteriograms. Left, With patient supine, filling of right renal artery is incomplete. Right, With patient upright, filling is complete.

Fig 2.—Humerus in external rotation (top) and internal rotation (bottom).

Arrows and other symbols should be noted parenthetically.

Fig 6.—Lateral view of right forearm two years after injury. Fracture of humerus has united (arrow).

A symbol or abbreviation that is used in more than one illustration must be explained in each of the legends of the figures in which it appears. When there are many symbols, a symbol "key" can be provided by the art department and included in the illustration. Otherwise, symbols and abbreviations may be explained in the legend.

If the author has provided several illustrations in which numerous abbreviations and symbols are repeated, a common key explaining the abbreviations should be provided in the first figure in which the abbreviations appear. The key should be referred to in subsequent legends as follows: For explanation of abbreviations, see key to Fig 1. In such a case, it is important that illustrations with a common key appear on facing pages. If illustrations appear on the following pages (back to back), the key must be repeated for the reader's convenience.

8.04—**Photomicrographs**—Indicate magnification and staining technique parenthetically at the end of the legend.

Fig 2.—Renal tubule after ischemic change ($\times 200$).

Fig 3.—Smear of aspirated bone marrow 14 weeks after transplant (Wright stain, $\times 600$).

Photomicrographs should not be reduced in most instances. If the size must be changed, that fact, together with original magnification, should be indicated in the legend. Note the extent of reduction in general terms (slightly, moderately, greatly). (Do not attempt to calculate the exact percentage of reduction.) Electron micrographs must always be reproduced within $\pm 5\%$ of the original size.

Fig 5.—Wedge-shaped cartilaginous lesions (Heidenhain azan, original magnification $\times 30$).

Fig 4.—Ocular inflammation 6 to 24 hours after immunologic challenge. Top, Nodular choroiditis, after six hours (Wright stain, original magnification, $\times 17$). Center, Diffuse choroidal polymorphonuclear leukocyte infiltration after 24 hours (Wright stain, original magnification, $\times 40$). Bottom, Higher magnification of center view showing polymorphonuclear leukocyte involvement (original magnification, $\times 150$).

8.05—**Case Numbers**—If an illustration refers to a particular case, include the case number in the legend.

Fig 1.—Fracture of right femur (case 6).

Fig 2.—Top, Case 6. Fracture of right femur. Bottom, Case 10. Fracture of left tibia.

8.06—**Dates**—Dates may be included in legends in accordance with the following forms.

Fig 3.—Upper shaft of right femur (March 14, 1974). Fracture is solidly united.

Fig 4.—Top, Huge aneurysm of left internal carotid artery on May 22, 1973. Bottom, Substantial reduction in size of aneurysm on Jan 11, 1974, after carotid ligation.

8.07—**Permission for Reproduction**—If an illustration has been used previously in another publication, written permission for its use must be obtained from the publisher (**25.00**). The source should be acknowledged. This may be included in the legend if it can be done briefly by citation of a reference. Otherwise, acknowledgment is made in a footnote at the end of the communication (**6.08**).

Fig 1.—Effect of chronic hepatic venous congestion (from Ayers et al[10]).

MATHEMATICAL COMPOSITION—9.00

Often, there is difficulty in the presentation of mathematical formulas and other expressions involving special symbols, character positions, and relationships. Helpful to both authors and copy editors are the *Style Manual of the American Institute of Physics*, the *Council of Biology Editors Style Manual*, and the University of Chicago's *A Manual of Style*. If a formula will occupy more than one column, it may be necessary to break it at an operation sign or to have it set across more than one column.

Long formulas may be handled either as copy or as prepared art, depending on the availability of special characters, the facility of composition, and the need for direct control of preparation.

9.01—**Copy Preparation**—Simple formulas given in the text may remain if no ambiguity for the Art/Layout Department, typesetter, or proofreader will result. Complicated formulas should be placed on a separate page and marked in detail both for alignment and characters.

If there are many equations in a report, they should be numbered consecutively.

When an equation is included in the text, it should appear on a separate line. All symbols should be defined and the units in which they are expressed should be stated, unless both the significance and the units are truly obvious from the context. Standard abbreviations should be used in expressing units of measure.

9.02—**Copy Marking**—It is essential to mark carefully each character, letter, and symbol that may be mistaken for an alternate form (X vs X vs χ), position (2 vs ^{2} vs $_2$), or identity (X vs $\times$). Most terms are set in italics. (See **20.02**.)

The following are correct markings for elements of equations:

superior $N_\vee^2$

inferior $N_\wedge$

inferior to superior $N_{\vee_1^{\wedge x}}$

superior to superior $N_{\vee\vee}^{x2}$

inferior to inferior $N_{r\wedge}$

superior to inferior N_{r}

inferior with superior
and subinferior N_{2}^{x}

9.03—**Simplifying**—Use a virgule (**14.14/1**) to avoid stacking of fractions whenever possible without sacrificing clarity.

$$y = (r_1 + r_2) / (p_1 - p_2), \text{ not } y = \frac{r_1 + r_2}{p_1 - p_2}$$

Use of radicals may sometimes be avoided by substitution of a fractional exponent.

$$(pq/n)^{1/2}, \text{ not } \sqrt{pq/n}$$

A negative exponent may simplify some expressions.

$$\frac{N}{(a+b)m} = N(a+b)^{-m}$$

Parentheses, brackets, and braces should be used to simplify expressions whenever possible.

$$E = 1.96\{[P(1-P)]/m\}^{\frac{1}{2}}, \text{ not } E = 1.96\sqrt{\frac{P(1-P)}{m}}$$

Long formulas may often be given in two or more lines by breaking them at operation signs outside brackets or parentheses and holding the indention whenever possible (since some formulas may be too long to permit indention).

$$Y = \left[(a_1 + B_1)/(a_2 - B_2)\right]$$
$$+ \left[(\sigma_1 + \sigma_2)/(\sigma_2 - \sigma_1)\right]$$
$$+ \left[(s_1 + s_2)/(t_1 + t_2)\right]$$

NB—Often, it is advisable to have formulas preset, to assure accuracy and proper placement in the text, and to provide the author with the final form prior to actual publication.

NOMENCLATURE—10.00

Cardiology—10.01

10.01/1—**Electrocardiographic Leads**—These symbols and designations are recommended by the American Heart Association:

Limb leads: I, II, III

Augmented leads: aV_R, aV_L, aV_F (Use lowercase *a*, full capital *V*, and subscript capitals *R*, *L*, and *F*.)

Chest leads: V_1, V_2, V_3, V_4, V_5, V_6. (Use subscript arabic numerals.)

Right-sided chest leads: V_{3R}, V_{4R}, V_{5R}, etc. (Both numeral and *R* are subscript.)

Lead from the back: V_B (subscript capital *B*).

Esophageal leads: V_{E34}, V_{E29} (subscripts *E34* and *E29* showing the distance in the esophagus of the electrode from the nares).

10.01/2—**Murmur Grades**—Intensity (loudness) of murmurs is designated by grades 1 through 6 (arabic numerals). A grade 1 murmur can be barely heard, a grade 3 murmur is moderately loud, and one of grade 6 is heard with the stethoscope just removed from the surface of the chest wall.

10.01/3—**Electrocardiographic Tracings, Segments, and Complexes**—The following examples show the proper style for use (or omission) of hyphens in ECG segment or complex specifications:

Incorrect	Correct
S-T segment	ST segment
S-T-T segment	ST-T segment
P-R segment	PR segment
Q-R-S complex	QRS complex

Complements—10.02

10.02/1—New symbols for the complement components of serum were announced at the 1973 International Congress of Immunology. (See also **10.09**.) Whereas the prime is no longer included and the designating number is set consistently on-line (not subscript), the style for complement specifications is as follows:

C1, C2, C3 . . . C9

NOMENCLATURE

Cranial Nerves—10.03

10.03/1—Use Roman numerals when designating cranial nerves, but ordinals when the adjectival form is used.

The cranial nerves (II, III, and VI) are protected by . . .

The second, third, and sixth cranial nerves are protected by . . .

10.03/2—English names are preferred in AMA style.

Nerve	English Name	Latin Name
I	Olfactory	Olfactorii
II	Optic	Opticus
III	Oculomotor	Oculomotorius
IV	Trochlear	Trochlearis
V	Trigeminal	Trigeminus
VI	Abducens	Abducens
VII	Facial	Facialis
VIII	Acoustic	Vestibulocochlearis
IX	Glossopharyngeal	Glossopharyngeus
X	Vagus	Vagus
XI	Spinal accessory	Accessorius
XII	Hypoglossal	Hypoglossus

Diseases—10.04

10.04/1—For correct names of diseases and syndromes, consult *Current Medical Information and Terminology (CMIT)*, *Dorland's Illustrated Medical Dictionary*, and *Stedman's Medical Dictionary*.

Distinguish between a disease and a syndrome.

hyaline membrane disease   tegmental syndrome

Hodgkin disease   Marfan syndrome

10.04/2—Eponyms should be avoided except when listed as preferred terminology in *CMIT*. If an author uses an unpreferred eponymic term, it may appear in parentheses after the preferred descriptive name at first mention in the synopsis-abstract or summary and at first mention in the text. (Note that the 's is not used with eponyms.)

diffuse interstitial pulmonary fibrosis (Hamman-Rich syndrome)

10.04/3—Capitalize an eponym but not the common noun associated with it **(4.08)**. Words derived from eponymic names of diseases are usually not capitalized **(4.07)**. Consult *Dorland's* or *Stedman's*.

Addison disease	Parkinson disease
addisonian	parkinsonism

10.04/4—A disease name derived from the name of an organism is not capitalized or italicized.

Infection with *Schistosoma* results in schistosomiasis.

Drugs—10.05

Because drugs may be referred to by several distinctive terms, persons concerned with the correct use of those terms should know the proper use and definition of each.

A *chemical* name describes a drug in terms of its chemical structure.

The *generic* name of a drug is its "nonproprietary" name, irrespective of its manufacturer.

The Trademark Act of 1946 defined *trade names* as "individual names and surnames, firm names and trade names used by manufacturers, industrialists . . . the names or titles lawfully adopted and used by persons, firms, associations, corporations, companies, unions." A trade name identifies a manufacturer but not necessarily a product.

A manufacturer's name for his product is called a *trademark*. The Trademark Act defined the term as "any word, name, symbol, or device or any combination thereof adopted and used by a manufacturer or merchant to identify his goods and distinguish them from those manufactured or sold by others."

Of imprecise legal standing is the term *brand name*, which may be found as an alternative to the term "trademark." The term *proprietary name* is also used.

10.05/1—The generic (nonproprietary) name of a drug should be used throughout a manuscript. Formally adopted generic names are given in *AMA Drug Evaluations*, *Pharmacopeia of the United States (USP)*, *National Formulary (NF)*, and *United States Adopted Names (USAN)*. In addition, the AMA Department of Drugs reports in *JAMA* (NEW

NAMES) drug names adopted by the USAN Council. These notices include both the generic names and trademarks for the newest drugs, usually prior to their publication elsewhere.

Available to editors of AMA scientific publications is the drug nomenclature printout, updated annually by the AMA Department of Drugs. The printout provides an alphabetical, cross-indexed listing of US and foreign code names, trademarks, and alternate nonproprietary names of drugs, as well as the formally approved nonproprietary names.

Where no generic name exists for a drug, give the chemical name or formula or description of the names of the active ingredients. If that terminology is unwieldy, the trademark may be used throughout the manuscript after the first mention.

If an author uses a chemical name or code number for a new unlisted drug, that use should be called to the attention of the AMA Department of Drugs and verified.

10.05/2—Use the complete name of a drug, including the salt or ester (eg, tetracycline hydrochloride, tetracycline phosphate complex, penicillin G potassium, penicillin O sodium), at first mention (in text and synopsis-abstract or summary) and elsewhere in contexts involving dosage. If in doubt regarding the form of the drug used, ask the author for more information.

In titles, inclusion of the salt or ester is neither necessary nor desirable—except in very special circumstances (eg, lithium carbonate, levomethadyl acetate). Always consult the Department of Drugs regarding drug names in titles.

10.05/3—A trademark used by the author should be placed in parentheses immediately after the first mention of the generic name, both in the text and in the synopsis-abstract or summary.

dactinomycin (Cosmegen)

Trademarks are capitalized, except for a few oddities (eg, pHisoHex). In mentioning trademarks in the text, follow the style in the examples given here. Note that when the salt is included in both the generic name and trademark (eg, tetracycline hydrochloride and Panmycin Hydrochloride), the salt is given only once, as in the first and second examples.

tetracycline (Panmycin) hydrochloride

penicillin O (Cer-O-Cillin) sodium

penicillin G potassium (Dramcillin)

If a foreign trademark is given, it should be noted in parentheses at first mention, together with the comparable US product.

phenprocoumon (Marcoumar [Canada]; Liquamar, comparable US product)

Trademarks should not be used elsewhere except as specified in **10.05/1** and **10.05/6**. When the author uses only generic names, ask author to specify trademarks.

10.05/4—Trademarks should be avoided in titles or subtitles of articles except in (1) monographs of the AMA Department of Drugs (2) adverse reaction reports, or (3) comparison of the same drug formulated by different manufacturers. (See also **19.04**.)

10.05/5—When US and foreign (600) generic names of a drug are listed, the preferred name (first-listed, printout 101) should be used. If the author uses an alternate term (printout 200), that term may appear in parentheses after first mention of the preferred name in the text and synopsis-abstract or summary.

leucovorin calcium (citrovorum factor)

If the author uses an alternate generic name *and* a trademark, both may appear in parentheses at first mention.

ascorbic acid (cevitamic acid; Cevalin)

Cyanocobalamin vs vitamin B$_{12}$: The substance used as a drug is cyanocobalamin; in food it is vitamin B$_{12}$.

Nitrogen mustard: Although nitrogen mustard is listed as an alternate name for mechlorethamine hydrochloride, the former term refers to a class of chemicals. As identification or description of a specific drug such as mechlorethamine hydrochloride, use the term "a nitrogen mustard" or "one of the nitrogen mustards." When only the general term is used, ask the author to specify the drug.

10.05/6—In major contributions, the names of some drugs mentioned in the text, tables, or legends are listed at the end of the text under the title "Nonproprietary Names and Trademarks of Drugs."

Drugs to be listed are these: (1) those given in the printout with the designation 101 AUC, 101 FDA, or 101 HEW, and (2) a drug that is the main subject of the article (eg, the drug name appears in the title).

Do not list a drug given in the printout as 101 USP or 101 ONF, or a drug for which both the nonproprietary (generic) name and trademarks are given in the text, tables, or legends, *except when the drug is the main subject of the article.*

Each generic name should be accompanied by all US trademarks listed in the nomenclature printout (400 series), unless the number is excessive. If more than six trademarks appear in the printout, list trademarks given in the *AMA Drug Evaluations.* Do not list a trademark that is identical with the nonproprietary name. Do not list foreign trademarks.

Complete drug names (generic and trademark) should be given, ie, including salts and esters. When the generic name and the trademark both include the same salt or ester (eg, hydrochloride), the name of the salt or ester should be repeated for each name. In the text, follow **10.05/3.**

Follow the style in the examples given here. Note that trademarks are listed alphabetically, that all parts of the trademarks are capitalized and italicized, and that a period is used at the end of each listing.

Nonproprietary Name and Trademark of Drug
Mafenide acetate—*Sulfamylon Cream.*

Nonproprietary Names and Trademarks of Drugs
Gentamicin sulfate—*Garamycin.*
Idoxuridine—*Dendrid, Herplex, Stoxil.*
Technetium Tc 99m sulfur colloid—*Colloscan-199m, Tesuloid Kit.*

10.05/7—Occasionally, an author may state that a patient was treated with "steroids," without identifying the drug or stating the dosage. Since different corticosteroids have different effects, and because there is controversy about the dosage in various therapeutic situations, the author should be asked to name the drug and give the dosage.

10.05/8—Do *not* expand *LSD* in titles, text, legends, or elsewhere. "Lysergic acid diethylamide" may be retained at first mention if used by the author.

Spell "marijuana" with a *j.*

Equipment—10.06

10.06/1—The use of trademarks (brand names) of manufactured items and names of manufacturers should be avoided when possible.

Most trademarks can be replaced by generic terms or descriptive phrases: "cellophane tape" for "Scotch tape"; "petroleum jelly" or "petrolatum" for "Vaseline." In some instances, however, the brand name must be retained as necessary information. (eg, Dacron, Teflon, Polaroid, Sephadex). After first mention of such a name, the trademark may be used alone.

10.06/2—When two or more brands of the same product are compared, brand names and manufacturers' names should be given.

10.06/3—Equipment or apparatus provided free of charge may be acknowledged in a footnote (**6.08**).

10.06/4—When a device is referred to as a "modified" type, the modification should be explained or an explanatory reference cited.

Genus and Species—10.07

10.07/1—For the correct names of genera and species and rules for forming plurals, consult *Bergey's Manual of Determinative Bacteriology* and *Bacterial and Mycotic Infections of Man* by Dubos and Hirsch.

10.07/2—After first mention of the singular form in the text, abbreviate genus name (without a period) when used with species, even when another species or genus is mentioned in the interim (**1.04**).

10.07/3—Italicize species, variety or subspecies, and genus when used in the singular. Do not italicize genus name when used in the plural. Do not italicize the name of a class, order, family, or tribe (**20.02/5**).

10.07/4—Capitalize genus in the singular, genus abbreviation, class, order, family, and tribe. In the text, do not capitalize species, variety, or subspecies, or plural forms of a genus name. In titles, capitalize the plural of a genus name, but do not capitalize name of species or subspecies (**4.16**).

10.07/5—If correct plural cannot be determined, add the word "organisms." (See also **13.05**.)

Salmonella enteritidis	*S typhimuri*	salmonellae
Treponema pallidum	*T genitalis*	treponemas
Proteus vulgaris	*P mirabilis*	*Proteus* organisms
Escherichia coli	*E aurescens*	*Escherichia* organisms

10.07/6—The abbreviation "sp" is a standard microbiological designation for "species," and it is used when the genus is certain but the species is not determined. For example, if the author knows that a skin test reaction occurs with *Toxocara* organisms but is uncertain about whether the elicited reaction results from the presence of *Toxocara canis* or *Toxocara cati*, he may write *Toxocara* sp, an accepted means for showing the uncertainty about species identification. The abbreviation "var" is acceptable when discussing variants of species.

Globulins—10.08

Globulins are a family of proteins precipitated from plasma or serum by half-saturation with ammonium sulfate. The globulins may be further fractionated by solubility and other separation methods into many subgroups. Use Greek letters and subscript numerals (where applicable) in designating globulins and globulin fractions.

NOMENCLATURE

α-globulin $\qquad$ α_1-globulin $\qquad$ α_2-globulin

β-globulin $\qquad\qquad\qquad$ γ-globulin

Immunoglobulins—10.09

An appropriate resource for information on immunoglobulins is Samter's *Immunological Diseases* (Little, Brown & Co, 1971).

10.09/1—The nomenclature for human immunoglobulins has undergone several revisions; follow that described in *Bulletin WHO* (48:373,1973).

10.09/2—Immunoglobulin and immune globulin are not synonymous. Immune globulins are sometimes called "antibodies"; the serum from which an antibody is derived can be called an "immune serum" or an "antiserum."

By absorption with immunoglobulin-specific antiserum, the antibody in secretions was shown to be primarily IgA.

"Immunoglobulin" is used chiefly to indicate the normal distribution of proteins, IgG, IgA, IgM, etc, as they occur in the serum. A γ-globulin preparation with known antibody activity is referred to as an "immune globulin."

Immunoglobulin chains are most often designated by the Greek letters κ and λ for the light chains and γ, α, μ for the heavy chains.

Class	Heavy Chain	Light Chain
IgG1	$\gamma1$	
IgG2	$\gamma2$	
IgG3	$\gamma3$	
IgG4	$\gamma4$	
IgA1	$\alpha1$	κ or $\lambda1$ or $\lambda2$
IgA2	$\alpha2$	
IgM	μ	
IgD	δ	
IgE	ϵ	

Isotopes—10.10

10.10/1—Isotope numbers are used in AMA publications principally in connection with radioactive drugs. When the isotope number is given for an element named by itself rather than as part of the name of a chemical compound, follow **10.10/2**. When the isotope number appears as part of the name of a compound, follow **10.10/3** if the compound has an approved nonproprietary drug name and **10.10/4** if it does not.

10.10/2—When an isotope is mentioned by itself rather than as part of the name of a chemical compound (a drug), there are two correct ways to name it: (1) when the name of the element is spelled out, the isotope number follows the name in the same typeface and type size (not as a superscript or subscript). The number is not preceded by a hyphen even in adjectival use. This is the preferred form for first mention of an isotope in the text or synopsis-abstract. (2) When the chemical symbol rather than the spelled out name of an element is used, the isotope number *precedes* the symbol as a *superscript*. (*Note:* A chemical symbol is not an abbreviation, and is never placed in parentheses after the spelled out first mention of the element without the isotope number.)

Who first discovered uranium 235?

Substances labeled with iodine 125 generally have the same uses as those containing iodine 131.

In its use as a drug (in the form of a colloid), radioactive gold (^{198}Au) should be referred to by its approved nonproprietary name: *gold Au 198*.

Of the 13 known isotopes of iodine, ^{128}I is the only one that is not radioactive.

Do not use the symbol representing a single element (eg, ^{74}As) as an abbreviation for a compound (eg, sodium arsenate As 74).

10.10/3—Approved nonproprietary names of drugs containing radioactive isotopes consist of three parts: (1) the name that would be used for the drug if it contained only stable isotopes, followed by (2) the chemical symbol of the element that is radioactive, followed by (3) the isotope number of the radioactive isotope. The isotope number appears in the same type (not superscript) as the rest of the drug name, and it is not preceded by a hyphen. When a drug has an approved nonproprietary name, that name is to be used in preference to other ways of referring to the drug.

Iodohippurate sodium I 131 (not radioactive iodohippurate sodium or ^{131}I-labeled iodohippurate sodium)

Exception: The approved nonproprietary name *tritiated water* omits the chemical symbol and isotope number. (See also **10.10/7**.)

10.10/4—A compound not having an approved nonproprietary drug name may be referred to in any of several descriptive ways.

Glucose labeled with radioactive carbon (^{14}C)

Glucose tagged with carbon 14

When the name of such a substance is abbreviated, use the superscript form of the isotope number, to the left of the chemical symbol.

Glucose ^{14}C (*not* glucose C 14)

10.10/5—In trademarks, isotope numbers usually appear in the same position as in approved nonproprietary names, but they are usually joined to the rest of the name by a hyphen, and they are not necessarily preceded by the chemical symbol. Follow the drug printout, *AMA Drug Evaluations*, and the usage of individual manufacturers.

Iodotope I 131   Cobatope-57

Glofil-125   Hippuran I-131

10.10/6—The abbreviation "ul" (for "uniformly labeled") may be used in parentheses to differentiate a preparation in which all molecules of a compound contain radioactive atoms from those preparations in which the radioactive material has merely been admixed to the compound to be labeled.

Glucose ^{14}C (ul)

This form should be used in place of such designations as "glucose-U-^{14}C."

10.10/7—Two isotopes of hydrogen have their own specific names, *deuterium* and *tritium*, which should be used instead of "hydrogen 2" and "hydrogen 3." In the text, the specific names should also be preferred to the symbols ^{2}H or D (for deuterium, which is stable) and ^{3}H (for tritium, which is radioactive). The two forms of heavy water (D_2O and ^3H_2O) should be referred to by the approved nonproprietary names *deuterium oxide* and *tritiated water*.

10.10/8—Except in trademarks, do not use the prefix *radio-* with the name of an element. Use the word *radioactive* instead.

10.10/9—**USAN Assigned to Radioactive Pharmaceuticals**—The United States Adopted Names (USAN) applicable to radioactive pharmaceuticals are composed of the name of the basic compound serving as the carrier for the radioactivity, the symbol for the radioactive isotope, and the atomic weight (since several radioactive isotopes of a given element may be in use—see listing under iodine). The following cumulative table of nonproprietary names is arranged in alphabetical order according to the English name of the radioactive element. The isotopes of hydrogen are listed under their specific names, deuterium and tritium. Radioactive pharmaceuticals are often supplied by the manufacturers under a designation equivalent to the adopted non-proprietary name and are listed as such in this table; specific trademarks are listed when they exist.

Isotope	Nonproprietary Name	Supplied As	Manufacturer
^{74}As	sodium arsenate As 74		
^{198}Au	gold Au 198	Gold Au 198	Mallinckrodt
		Aureotope	Squibb
^{45}Ca	calcium chloride Ca 45		
^{131}Cs	cesium chloride Cs 31		
^{51}Cr	chromated Cr 51 serum albumin	Chromalbin	Squibb
	chromic chloride Cr 51		
	chromic phosphate Cr 51		
	sodium chromate Cr 51	Sodium Chromate Cr 51	Mallinckrodt
		Chromitope Sodium	Squibb
^{57}Co	cobaltous chloride Co 57	Cobatope-57	Squibb
	cyanocobalamin Co 57	Racobalamin-57	Abbott
		Cyanocobalamin Co 57	Mallinckrodt
		Rubratope-57	Squibb
^{60}Co	cobaltous chloride Co 60	Cobatope-60	Squibb
	cyanocobalamin Co 60	Rubratope-60	Squibb
^{64}Cu	cupric acetate Cu 64		
^{67}Ga	gallium citrate Ga 67	Gallium Citrate Ga 67	New England Nuclear
^{2}H	deuterium oxide (stable isotope)		
^{125}I	diatrizoate sodium I 125		
	diohippuric acid I 125		
	diotyrosine I 125		
	human growth hormone I 125	Human Growth Hormone I 125	Abbott
	insulin I 125		
	iodinated I 125 serum albumin	Radioiodinated (I_{125}) Serum Albumin (Human) IHSA 125	Mallinckrodt
		Albumotope I-125	Squibb
	iodopyracet I 125		
	iomethin I 125		
	iothalamate sodium I 125	Glofil-125	Abbott
	liothyronine I 125	Triomet-125	Abbott
	oleic acid I 125	Oleic Acid I 125	Mallinckrodt
	povidone I 125		
	sodium iodide I 125	Sodium Iodide I 125	Mallinckrodt
	thyroxine I 125	Thyroxine I 125	Mallinckrodt
		Tetramet-125	Abbott

Isotope	Nonproprietary Name	Supplied As	Manufacturer
^{131}I	ethiodized oil I 131		
	iodinated I 131 serum albumin	Radioiodinated (I_{131}) Serum Albumin (Human) IHSA 131	Mallinckrodt
		Albumotope I-131	Squibb
	iodinated I 131 serum albumin aggregated	Macroscan-131	Abbott
		Aggregated Radioiodinated (I_{131}) Albumin (Human) MAA I 131	Mallinckrodt
		Albumotope-LS	Squibb
	iodipamide sodium I 131		
	iodoantipyrine I 131		
	iodohippurate sodium I 131	Hippuran-131	Abbott
		Hippuran I 131	Mallinckrodt
		Hipputope	Squibb
	iotyrosine I 131		
	rose bengal sodium I 131	Sodium Rose Bengal I 131	Mallinckrodt
		Robengatope	Squibb
	sodium iodide I 131	Oriodide-131	Abbott
		Oriodide-131-H	Abbott
		Radiocaps-131	Abbott
		Theriodide-131	Abbott
		Sodium Iodide I 131	Mallinckrodt
		Iodotope	Squibb
		Iodotope Therapeutic	Squibb
	tolpovidone I 131		
	triolein I 131	Triolein I 131	Mallinckrodt
^{192}Ir	iridium Ir 192		
^{59}Fe	ferric chloride Fe 59	Ferric Chloride Fe 59	Mallinckrodt
	ferrous citrate Fe 59	Ferrous Citrate Fe 59	Mallinckrodt
	ferrous sulfate Fe 59		
^{42}K	potassium chloride K 42		
^{85}Kr	krypton clathrate Kr 85		
^{3}H	tritiated water		
^{197}Hg	chlormerodrin Hg 197	Chlormerodrin Hg 197	Mallinckrodt
		Chlormerodrin Hg 197	Squibb
	merisoprol Hg 197		
	merisoprol acetate Hg 197		
^{203}Hg	chlormerodrin Hg 203	Chlormerodrin Hg 203	Mallinckrodt
^{32}P	chromic phosphate P 32	Chromic Phosphate P 32	Abbott
		Phosphocol P 32	Mallinckrodt
	polymetaphosphate P 32		
	sodium phosphate P 32	Sodium Phosphate P 32	Mallinckrodt
		Phosphotope	Squibb

Isotope	Nonproprietary Name	Supplied As	Manufacturer
^{86}Rb	rubidium chloride Rb 86		
^{75}Se	selenomethionine Se 75	Selenomethionine Se 75	Mallinckrodt
		Sethotope	Squibb
^{22}Na	sodium chloride Na 22		
^{85}Sr	strontium chloride Sr 85		
	strontium nitrate Sr 85	Strontium Nitrate Sr 85	Mallinckrodt
		Strotope	Squibb
^{35}S	sodium sulfate S 35		
^{99m}Tc	sodium pertechnetate Tc 99m	Sodium Pertechnetate Tc99m	Mallinckrodt
		Sodium Pertechnetate Tc99m	New England Nuclear
	technetium Tc 99m	Elutex	Abbott
		Ultra-TechneKow/Ultra-Technekow FM Generator	Mallinckrodt
		Neimotec	Mallinckrodt
		Technetope	Squibb
		Minitec	Squibb
		Tc99m Generator	New England Nuclear
	technetium Tc 99m albumin aggregated		
	technetium Tc 99m sulfur colloid	Technetium 99m Sulfur Colloid	Mallinckrodt
		Technetium 99m Sulfur Colloid	New England Nuclear
		Collokit	Abbott
^{133}Xe	xenon Xe 133	Xeneisol 133	Mallinckrodt
^{169}Yb	pentetate trisodium calcium Yb 169	Pentetate Trisodium Calcium Yb 169	Minnesota Mining & Mfg Co
^{65}Zn	zinc chloride Zn 65		

Vertebrae—10.11

10.11/1—For preferred terminology, consult *Dorland's Illustrated Medical Dictionary* and *Stedman's Medical Dictionary*.

10.11/2—In reports of clinical or technical data and in tables, specific designations of vertebrae and intervertebral spaces may be abbreviated without first being written out, if no confusion results. Abbreviate in accordance with these examples:

vertebrae: C-2   L-2   S-2   T-2
spaces: C2-3   L2-3   S2-3   T2-3

Uniformity has not been clearly established for capitalization, spacing, and phrasing of virus designations. Some preferred forms are listed here. Note that Arabic numerals are used, not Roman. Alphabetical designations of virus groups or types are capitalized.

picornavirus   myxovirus   herpesvirus   arbovirus

enterovirus   rhinovirus   poliovirus   adenovirus

influenza virus   type A influenza virus

echovirus   echovirus 30   echoviruses 29 and 32

coxsackievirus   coxsackieviruses A and B

coxsackieviruses B3 and B5, or

coxsackievirus B types 3 and 5, or

group B coxsackieviruses 3 and 5

simian virus 40 (SV 40)   Giles virus   Frater virus

The following is a useful reference on virus nomenclature: Wildy P: *Classification and Nomenclature of Viruses, First Report of the International Committee on Nomenclature of Viruses.* Basel, Switzerland, S Karger AG, 1971.

NUMBERS—11.00

11.01—In titles, subtitles, and text, spell out all numbers from one through ten and use Arabic numerals for all numbers greater than ten, except as specified in **11.02-11.14.**

11.02—Round numbers in millions, billions, and tenths and hundredths of billions are written as follows:

1 million   2.5 million $3 billion   4.5 billion

4.55 billion   (*But:* 1,510,000   4,555,000,000).

11.03—Use Arabic numerals for the following:

    A. **Addresses**—House and room numbers. Numbered streets are written as ordinals. Spell out *first* through *tenth*; use numerals for *11th* and above. (See also **10.10.**)

10 Edgewood Lane   1329 E Fifth St

Room 654, Palmolive Bldg   8 Tenth Ave

B. **Ages**

She brought her 3-month-old baby.

The boy was 9 years old, eight years younger than his nearest sibling aged 17.

C. **Chapter, page, and line numbers**

chapter 3   page 85   line 10

D. **Numbers as designators**

day 10   treatment protocol 5

E. **Dates**—Do not use numerals for months except in tables (**18.03**). Do not use ordinals in dates. Convert military/European date forms (eg, 29 Aug 1973) to conventional form (Aug 29, 1973).

F. **Decimals**—Place a zero before a decimal point in numbers less than one, except in special cases where customary usage omits it. (See also **18.05**).

6.5 in   0.3 gm

(*But:* .22-caliber rifle, $P<.05$, $r=.86$)

When material (in text or tables) includes both whole numbers and numbers with decimal fractions, use a decimal point and zero(s) with the whole numbers to indicate the accuracy level of the data (but verify this change with author). Generally, in any one category of material (eg, average age, number of patient-years, or percentage), each numerical entry should include the same number of decimal places.

The percentage of failures ranged from 29.6% in 1941 to 59.0% in 1961.

Measurements of 5.3 and 6.0 cm were recorded.

G. **Figure and table numbers**

Results are shown in Fig. 3.

Correlation was not statistically significant ($P>.05$, Table 6).

H. **Mixed fractions**

He waited 3½ hours.

He walked 6¾ blocks.

But note: Common fractions should be spelled out. When used with an abbreviated unit of measure, a quantity less than one should usually be expressed as a decimal, eg, 0.5 gm.

half of the cases   a three-fourths filled jar

two thirds of the diagnoses   two-thirds majority

I. **Percentages**

A 5% incidence is common.

Do not omit percent sign with zero. (See also **12.00**.)

The reported incidence varies from 0% to 5%.

J. **All quantities (1 or more) with units of measure,** except time.

The node measured 4 cm in diameter.

He was given 2 gm of tetracycline orally.

Thoracocentesis yielded 2 liters of fluid.

The procedure was continued for three days.

K. **Sums of money**—When no fraction of a dollar is given, do not use ciphers or period. (See also **11.02**.)

He paid $8.97 for the groceries and $9 for the medicine.

What can you buy for 5 cents?

L. **Thermometer degrees** (Do not use degree sign.)

If his temperature is 37.8 C (100.0 F), he has a fever of 0.8 C (1.4 F).

The plates were cultured at 20 C.

M. **Time of day when followed by AM or PM**—Do not use ciphers or colon when full hour is given.

The plane leaves Chicago at 11:05 AM and arrives in Providence, RI, at 2 PM.

(*But:* Tea was served at four o'clock.)

Exception: The needle was inserted at the 4-o'clock position. (See **5.09**.)

11.04—Whenever the numerator/denominator ingredients of a proportion, rate, ratio, or percentage are cited in the form "*n/d,*" do not convert to "*n* of *d.*"

Death occurred in 30% (6/20) of the patients.

11.05—At the beginning of a sentence, all numbers must be spelled out, even though similar or coordinate numbers are written as numerals elsewhere in the same sentence.

Twenty-five institutions were participants in this cooperative study.

Forty-seven patients were hospitalized, 34 were treated as outpatients, and 53 required no further therapy.

Note: Omit "and" in spelled out compound numbers.

One hundred twelve cases.

One hundred twenty-eight men and 85 women were included in the study. (Sentence may be reworded: The study included 128 men and 85 women.)

11.06—When a unit of measure follows a number at the beginning of a sentence, it too must be written out, even though the same unit is abbreviated elsewhere in the same sentence.

Fifteen milligrams of the drug was administered at 9 PM and 25 mg at 3:30 AM.

Two hundred to eight hundred picograms per milliliter is the range of normal levels of vitamin B_{12}.

Note: A better version of the sentence would read as follows:

The range of normal levels of vitamin B_{12} is 200 to 800 pg/ml.

11.07—Use arabic numerals whenever numbers are presented as part of a quantitative array (three numbers or more in a series), even if none of the individual numbers exceeds ten.

In March, April, and May the manager added 9, 7, and 1 employees, respectively.

11.08—When one numerical expression immediately follows another, spell out the one that can be more easily expressed in words, or reword the sentence. (See also **14.04/10.**)

He bought eleven 95-cent brushes.

In the first group of fifteen hundred, 690 were symptom-free.

In the first group, 690 of the 1,500 patients were symptom-free.

11.09—Do not omit digits when indicating a span of years or pages.

    1963-1964   pp 1181-1189

    1963 to 1967   pages 1181 to 1189

11.10—Ordinals *first* through *tenth* are always spelled out; those greater than tenth are expressed as numerals, except at the beginning of a sentence. (See also **11.07**.)

    I have asked my 15th question without waiting for answers to my 4th, 9th, and 13th questions.

    Only the Fifth Battalion responded.

    The 5th, 9th, and 12th battalions responded.

    Eleventh-grade pupils may leave early.

11.11—Roman numerals are used with proper names. Note that *no comma* is used before the numeral.

    Henry Ford III   Friendship VII   Louis XIV

11.12—Avoid the use of Roman numerals except when part of formally established terminology, such as blood-clotting factors, cardiac enlargement or hypertrophy, cranial nerves, ECG leads, hyperlipoproteinemia types, and streptococcus group B types. Use Arabic numerals for platelet factors, heart murmurs, organism or virus types, and with "para," "gravida," and "abortus."

blood-clotting factor VII	lead II
platelet factor 3	para 1
coxsackievirus B2	gravida 2
echovirus 30	abortus 2
hyperlipoproteinemia type III	grade 2/6

Use Roman numerals for cancer stages; use Arabic for cancer grades. In pedigree charts, Roman numerals are used to indicate generations, Arabic numerals to indicate families or individual family members.

11.13—In bibliographic material (ie, references, book reviews), do not use Roman numerals to indicate volume number, even though Roman numerals may have been used in the original. Page numbers given in lowercase Roman numerals referring to pages in a foreword, preface, or introduction should be retained.

11.14—For the use of Roman numerals in the Bible and other classic references, follow the most recent edition of the University of Chicago's *A Manual of Style*. (See also **15.40**.)

11.15—Divisions of a short enumeration are run-in and indicated by numerals or lowercase italic letters enclosed within parentheses.

Paragraphed numbers followed by a period without parentheses may be used for long or complex enumerations.

For an enumeration in which items are subdivided, follow a modified outline style.

PERCENT—12.00

The term "percent" derives from Latin *per centum*, meaning by the hundred, or in, to, or for every hundred. ("Percentage" is an extension of the term, and means "a number or amount stated in percent." "Percentile" is a statistical term for the value in a distribution of frequencies divided into 100 equal groups.

12.01—Use the symbol, %, and Arabic numerals for percentages. The symbol is set close; it is repeated with each number in a series or range. If the percentage term occurs at the beginning of a sentence, the numeral and the symbol should be spelled out, or the sentence should be reworded to retain the numeral and symbol.

4.7%   5%-15%   1.6%, 4.3%, and 16.9%   vol%

Twenty-seven percent of the patients survived.

Heart disease was present in a small percent of the subjects.

These values were compared with the percentages in 1950.

12.02—If percentages are used by the author in a series that includes fewer than 100 subjects, the actual number of subjects should also be given for each percentage.

in 73% (19) of the 26 patients studied, *or*

in 19 (73%) of the 26 patients studied

Do not use decimals in showing percentages in a series that includes fewer than 1,000 subjects.

12.03—A discrepancy in the sum of percentages in a tabulation should be called to the attention of the author and accounted for in a footnote.

PLURALS—13.00

13.01—**Abbreviations**—For units of measure, use the same abbreviation for singular and plural forms. (See **1.02, 14.01/3.**) For most all-cap abbreviations, the plural is formed by adding *s*.

RBCs   WBCs   HMOs   PSROs   EEGs   IQs

*But:*Do not use the abbreviation or its plural form to denote a person by title or status.

Wrong: Three MDs reported. *Correct:* Three physicians reported.

13.02—**Collective Nouns**—Collective nouns may be either singular or plural, depending on the intended meaning.

A number of subjects were unavailable for follow-up.

The number of controls was small.

The majority rules.

The majority were cured.

With units of measure always use singular.

Five milliliters *was* injected.

13.03—**Compounds**—Follow *Webster's International Dictionary* for proper formation of plural compounds.

courts-martial   attorneys-at-law

attorneys general   brothers-in-law

13.04—**Latin and Greek vs English**—Follow *Webster's International Dictionary* for plural forms of Latin and Greek words. Use the English form when given.

13.05—**Organisms**—Use the lowercase plural form for those organisms that have a common designation. (See also **10.07/5.**)

Singular	**Plural**
Bacillus	bacilli
Staphylococcus	staphylococci
Streptococcus	streptococci

For those organisms that do not have a common plural designation, insert the word "organisms" or "sp" to indicate a plural use. (See also **10.07/6**.)

Enterobacter organisms   *Pseudomonas* sp

Xenopsylla sp

PUNCTUATION—14.00

Apostrophe—14.01

14.01/1—Use the apostrophe to show the possessive case in accordance with these examples:

Essex' execution	children's wants
Caesar's Palace	Jones's bones (one Jones)
an hour's wait	the Joneses' bones (two or more Joneses)
three hours' wait	Moses' law
a child's wants	

(*But:* Hodgkin disease [see **10.04/2**].)

14.01/2—Use '*s* to indicate the plural of words or letters spoken of as such.

He uses too many *and*'s.

Mind your *p*'s and *q*'s.

14.01/3—Do not use an apostrophe to form the plural of an all-cap abbreviation or of numerals, including dates (years). (See also **1.02, 13.01**.)

ECGs   EEGs   IQs   WBCs   RBCs

A young man in his 20s

During the early 1960s

The Roaring 20s

14.01/4—Do not use an apostrophe to indicate the plural of a name.

14.01/5—Do not use an apostrophe where a prime is intended. (Do not use a prime as a symbol of measurement.)

PUNCTUATION

Brackets—14.02

14.02/1—Use brackets to indicate editorial interpolation within a quotation.

"Enough questions had arisen [these are not described] to warrant medical consultation."

Thompson stated, "Because of the patient's age and debility, *surgery* was postponed" [italics added].

"The following year [1947] was a turning point."

"Breathing of the gas is often followed by extraordinary fits of extacy [sic]."

14.02/2—Use brackets to indicate parentheses within parentheses.

A nitrogen mustard (mechlorethamine [Mustargen] hydrochloride) was one of the drugs used.

14.02/3—In chemical and mathematical formulas, parentheses are generally used for the innermost units, with brackets and then braces added if necessary. When braces are used, they should appear as the outermost enclosure. (See also **9.03**.)

1-(10-{3-[4-(2-hydroxyethyl)-1-piperazinyl]propyl}-phenothiazin-2-yl)-1-propanone bis (hydrogen maleate)

14.02/4—When a parenthetical or bracketed insertion in the text contains a formula in which parentheses or brackets appear, the symbols within the formula should be left as given unless that would place two identical symbols immediately adjacent. To avoid adjacent identical symbols, change parentheses to brackets or brackets to parentheses in the formula as needed.

The chemical name of pyroxamine maleate (3-[p-Chloro-α-phenylbenzyl)oxy]-1-methylpyrrolidine maleate) is a good example.

The equation suggested by this phenomenon ($t=d/[r_1-r_2]$) can be applied in a variety of circumstances.

Colon—14.03

The colon is used to indicate some degree of coordination in a series of elements.

14.03/1—Use a colon to separate two main clauses when the second contains an illustration or amplification of the first.

The little boy had reason to cry: he had lost his dog.

This question must be answered: does the end justify the means?

14.03/2—If more than one grammatically independent statement follows the colon, these may be treated as separate sentences and the initial words capitalized (**4.13**).

> The most important questions have not been answered: What is the cause? What will be the outcome?

> (*But:* The views he expressed were absurd: Science and religion are incompatible; all artists are wealthy; and the rich are always wicked.)

> (*Or:* He expressed the views that science and religion are incompatible, that all artists are wealthy, and that the rich are always wicked [**14.03/4**].)

14.03/3—Use a colon to introduce an enumeration, especially after anticipatory phrasing such as *thus, as follows, the following.* (But see also **14.03/4**.)

> The following articles will be needed: pencil, paper, and eraser.

> He favored the legislation for three reasons: (1) It would benefit the small-town physician. (2) It would permit freer access to hospitals. (3) It would enable the intern to acquire broader experience.

> A wooden noose is made as follows: First, cut an ash bough and bend it into a loop. Then tie the ends together and peel the bark.

14.03/4—Do not use a colon if the sentence is continuous without it. A colon should not separate a preposition or a verb (including *to be* in all its manifestations) from its object. Do not use a colon after *because.*

> You will need pencil, paper, and eraser.

> The necessary articles include pencil, paper, and eraser.

> The train stops at Springfield, Worcester, and Boston.

> He left the clinic because the facilities were inadequate, the record system was inefficient, and the nurses were poorly trained.

> Alcohol is commonly used (1) as topical antiseptic, (2) as a solvent, and (3) as a fuel.

14.03/5—Use a colon to introduce a formal or extended quotation.

> Concluding his address, the chairman stated: "The past is dim; the future is bright with hope."

> Lincoln rose and spoke: "Fourscore and seven years ago . . ."

14.03/6—Use a colon to separate chapter and verse numbers in biblical references, hours and minutes in expressions of time, and parts of numerical ratios.

The story begins in Genesis 5:28.

The helicopter took off promptly at 6:55 AM.

In this region the ratio of births to deaths is 13:11.

14.03/7—In references, use a colon (1) between name(s) of author(s) and title; (2) between title and subtitle; and (3) for periodicals, between volume and page numbers. (See also **15.00.**)

Comma—14.04

14.04/1—The comma is used as a mark of separation within a sentence to make clear the groupings of words, phrases, and clauses with regard to (1) the grammatical structure and (2) the intended meaning.

In general, commas are used (1) after opening clauses or long opening phrases, (2) to set off nonrestrictive subordinate clauses or nonrestrictive participial phrases, and (3) to avoid mistaken or awkward junction within a sentence.

If the patient shows no adverse reaction, the dosage may be increased. (*But:* The dosage may be increased if the patient shows no adverse reaction.)

After long delay and many false starts, the investigation is finally under way.

Remembering his earlier encounter with the medication, he was reluctant to begin therapy again.

I think the wound must be painful, because he limps. (*But:* He limps because the wound is painful.)

The eldest son, who was in Seattle at the time, wired congratulations. (*But:* Only the son who lives in Chicago was present at the ceremony.)

Improvement was noted in all patients, including those who had required hospitalization previously.

Correlation between body build and hirsutism was made, with no substantive results.

For Mary, Anthony would do his best.

Ever since, he has been interested in medicine.

Inside, the fire burned brightly.

Whenever possible, treatment is directed toward the underlying disease.

The patients withstood the complications of combined cancer chemotherapy, and treatment has been discontinued. (*But:* The patients withstood the complications of combined cancer chemotherapy and eventually treatment was discontinued.) Omission of the comma in the second example will not result in confusion.

14.04/2—In a simple series or enumeration, separate the elements by commas, including a comma before *and, or,* or *nor*. (See also **14.03/3, 14.13/3**.)

Red, blue, and yellow are primary colors.

You can go by boat, by train, or by helicopter.

He asked the patient where she had found the berries, what color they were, and why she had eaten them.

There were four contributing factors: (1) excessive drinking, (2) lack of sleep, (3) improper diet, and (4) obesity.

14.04/3—When an enumeration occurs in the name of a business firm, the comma is usually omitted before the ampersand. However, follow the punctuation used by the individual firm, except in references (**15.27**.)

Smith Kline & French Laboratories

Holt, Rinehart & Winston, Inc

14.04/4—Use commas to set off *viz, ie, eg,* and the expanded equivalents, *namely, that is,* and *for example*.

Cutaneous reactions may be noted, eg, hives, flushing, pruritus.

14.04/5—Use commas to set off parenthetical words, phrases, and other expressions that interrupt the continuity of a sentence, eg, *therefore, moreover, on the other hand, of course, to tell the truth, nevertheless, after all, consequently, to say the least, however*.

It was impossible, of course, to reevaluate the earlier sample.

His honesty and sincerity are commendable, to say the least.

However, much as I try, I cannot understand Einstein's theory. (*But:* However much I try, I cannot understand Einstein's theory.)

Therefore, he drew the correct conclusion. (*But:* He therefore drew the correct conclusion.)

14.04/6—Academic degrees; titles, and Jr and Sr are set off by commas when they follow the name of a person. (See also **1.06; 1.07; 4.02; 11.11.**)

> Arthur K. Brown, Jr, PhD, a biometrician, did the statistical analysis.
>
> (*But:* John D. Rockefeller III; Henry VIII.)

14.04/7—Use commas to separate the elements in an address.

> For further information, write to William M. Jones, 540 N State St, Chicago, IL 60610.

Omit the commas after the name of a person when *of* is used.

> Carl M. Jones of Des Moines, Iowa, is secretary of the association.

14.04/8—In dates and similar expressions of time, use commas according to the following examples. Note that no commas are used when month and year are given without the day. (See also **1.15.**)

> Results of a survey made in November 1968 were inconclusive.
>
> The patient was seen first on Dec 9, 1973, and again on Jan 22, 1974.
>
> The building will be closed at 10 PM, Friday, May 29.
>
> They were married on New Year's Day, 1957.

14.04/9—Separate digits with a comma to indicate thousands.

> 1,234   12,345   615,478   9,473,209

14.04/10—Occasionally, a comma may be used to separate adjacent unrelated numerals if neither can be expressed easily in words. (See also **11.08.**) Usually, it is preferable to reword the sentence and/or spell out one of the numbers.

> In 1929, 1,250,000 investors were wiped out.
>
> In 1929 a total of 1,250,000 investors were wiped out.
>
> (*But:* There were twelve 85-year-old men in the group.)

14.04/11—Do not use a comma between two units of the same dimension.

> 6 ft 2 in   4 lb 2 oz   3 yr 4 mo

14.04/12—The comma is placed inside quotation marks and before superscript citation of references and footnote symbols.

Dashes—14.05

Dashes include hyphens (**14.08**), em dashes, en dashes, 2-em dashes, and 3-em dashes.

Em Dash

14.05/1—Use a period and an em dash after sideheads and after numerical designation in table titles and figure legends.

> **Fibrinolysis.**—Increase in spontaneous fibrinolytic activity was noted.

> Fig 2.—Three months later.

> CASE 4.—A 4-year-old girl was first seen on Aug 20, 1963.

> Table 2.—Incidence of Bleeding Episodes.

14.05/2—Use an em dash in listing the nonproprietary names and trademarks of drugs at the end of an article.

> Furosemide—*Lasix.*

> Disodium edetate—*Endrate, Sodium Versenate.*

14.05/3—Use an em dash before designation "ED." in an editor's note.

> *These comments have been abstracted from two letters received from Dr Benson.*—ED.

14.05/4—Use a period and an em dash after the opening words in LETTERS TO THE EDITOR.

> *To the Editor.—   In Reply.—*

14.05/5—Use em dashes sparingly to indicate interruption in the sequence of a sentence. Do not use an em dash when another punctuation mark will suffice.

> All of these factors—age, severity of symptoms, psychic preparation, and choice of anesthetic agent—determine the patient's reaction.

14.05/6—An em dash may be used to separate referents from a pronoun that is the subject of an ending clause.

> Osler, Billings, and Jacobi—these were the men he tried to emulate.

En Dash

14.05/7—Use the en dash to show relational distinction in a hyphenated modifier.

> Winston-Salem–oriented group
> physician-lawyer–directed section

2-Em Dash

14.05/8—The 2-em dash may be used to separate independent statements in a paragraph.

> These items were noted: Graham Smith, MD, was the youngest member of his class; he was certified by the American Board of Pediatrics in 1951, and he won the Judson Prize in 1960.—— Pearson Jones, MD, was licensed by reciprocity, is in general practice, and has never published his findings, despite extensive personal research.——Franklin Piedicue, MD, started his graduate work at the age of 38 and has served as missionary in West Africa since getting his MD degree in 1966.

3-Em Dash

14.05/9—The 3-em dash is used to show exclusion of information in the text. (It is not used in references.)

> Our study began in N———, noted for its casual life-style.

> I admire Dr ——— too much to expose him in this anecdote.

Ellipses—14.06

14.06/1—Use ellipses (three periods separated by spaces) to indicate omissions from quoted material.

> If omission occurs after completion of a sentence ending in a period, use ellipses in addition, ie, four periods separated by spaces.

> Omit ellipses at beginning and end of a quotation if the quoted portion can be read as a complete sentence.

> Omit ellipses within a quotation when the omitted words occur at the same place as a bracketed editorial insertion (**14.02**).

14.06/2—In tables, ellipses may be used to indicate that no data were available or that a specified category of data is not applicable. (See also **18.05**.)

Exclamation Mark—14.07

14.07/1—Except in direct quotations and in rare and special circumstances, use of the exclamation mark should be avoided.

> The !Kung Bushmen live in Botswana.

In mathematical expressions, the exclamation mark is used to show a factorial number.

$$n = 5! = 5 \times 4 \times 3 \times 2 \times 1$$

Hyphen—14.08

The trend continues toward combining the elements of a compound (two or more words used as a single term) into one unhyphenated word. No simple rules can prescribe precisely, for all circumstances, when to use a hyphen or when to write a term as one word or as separate words. For compounds in common usage, follow the current edition of *Webster's International Dictionary*.

A few rules are given here as guides. They should not be construed as absolute. In general, when not otherwise specified, hyphens should be used only as an aid to the reader's understanding, primarily to avoid ambiguity. For capitalization of hyphenated compounds in titles, subtitles, subheads, and table heads, see **4.12**.

14.08/1—A compound adjective or adjective phrase is often (but not always) hyphenated when preceding the noun it modifies. The same modifier is often not hyphenated when it follows the noun. (See also **14.08/2-4; 14.08/12-19**.)

This is an up-to-date book.
This book is up to date.

An end-to-end anastomosis was made.
An anastomosis was made end to end.

a 5-year-old boy
a boy who is 5 years old

a well-fed infant
an infant who is well fed

foreign-born residents
residents who are foreign born

a low-quality yield
a yield of low quality

a follicle-stimulating hormone

a dark-red lesion

long-term therapy

the syringe-and-needle method

PUNCTUATION

A. In the following examples, note use of hyphen to avoid ambiguity:

an older-car owner (owner of an older car)

an older car owner (car owner who is older)

a small-bowel constriction (constriction of the small bowel)

a small bowel constriction (small constriction of the bowel)

B. Some combinations of words are commonly read together as a unit. Used as modifiers, these combinations should not be hyphenated.

birth control methods	open heart surgery
public health officials	bone marrow biopsy
medical school students	urinary tract infection
social service agency	cerebrospinal fluid cells

C. Do not hyphenate names of disease entities used as modifiers.

grand mal seizures	hyaline membrane disease
basal cell sarcoma	sickle cell anemia
myocardial infarction invalidism	sickle cell trait

(*But:* multiple-sclerosis-like, **14.05/7**.)

14.08/2—Do not use a hyphen after an adverb ending in *ly* even when used in a compound modifier preceding the word modified.

the clearly stated purpose   a highly developed species

14.08/3—Hyphenate a combination of two or more adjectives used coordinately or as conflicting terms, either when preceding or when following the noun modified.

There were blue-black lesions.

The lesions were blue-black.

He had a manic-depressive psychosis.

His psychosis was thought to be manic-depressive.

false-positive results

81

results that were false-positive

herpesvirus-positive reaction

of German-French-Irish ancestry

The serum was HB$_s$Ag-negative.

double-blind study

14.08/4—Do not hyphenate names of chemical compounds used as adjectives.

sodium chloride solution   tannic acid test

(*But:* hematoxylin-eosin stain)

14.08/5—Most combinations of proper adjectives derived from geographical entities are not hyphenated.

Central Americans   the Far East

Central American customs   Far Eastern customs

(*But:* Latin-Americans; Latin-American customs)

14.08/6—Do not hyphenate Latin expressions used in an adjective sense. Most of these are spaced out as separate words; a few are joined without a hyphen. Follow *Webster's New Collegiate Dictionary.*

an a priori argument   per diem employees

prima facie evidence   postmortem examination

an ex officio member   antebellum days

in vivo specimens   carcinoma in situ

14.08/7—Hyphenate a combination of two nouns used coordinately as a unit modifier when preceding the noun but not when following.

albumin-globulin ratio   (*But:* ratio of albumin to globulin)

the Binet-Simon test   (*But:* the test of Binet and Simon)

14.08/8—Hyphenate a combination of two nouns of equal participation used as a single noun.

player-manager   author-critic

soldier-statesman   physician-poet

14.08/9—Hyphenate most compound nouns containing a particle or prepositional phrase. Follow *Webster's International Dictionary.*

PUNCTUATION

a tie-in   a tie-up   a go-between

mother-in-law   a looker-on   a hand-me-down

(But: a passerby, a handout, an onlooker)

14.08/10—Hyphenate compounds in which the first element is a possessive.

bird's-eye view   crow's-feet   bull's-eye

14.08/11—Join without a hyphen most common prefixes (*ante, anti, bi, co, contra, counter, de, inter, micro, mid, non, over, pre, post, pro, pseudo, re, sub, super, trans, tri, ultra, un*) and common suffixes (*fold, hood, less, wise*), except as noted in **14.08/12–14.08/15.**

antivivisection   manhood   posttraumatic

clockwise   midaxillary   repossess

coauthor   nonnegotiable   shoeless

coexistence   nonresident   transsacral

coidentity   overproduction   twofold

countertendency   postoperative   ultramicroscopic

(But: by-line, co-opt, co-sponsor, co-worker, intra-aortic)

14.08/12—Use a hyphen with a prefix before a proper noun.

anti-American   pseudo-Christian

14.08/13—Use a hyphen after a prefix when the unhyphenated word would have a different meaning.

re-treat   re-creation

14.08/14—Occasionally, a hyphen is used after a prefix or before a suffix to avoid an awkward combination of letters. Follow *Webster's International Dictionary.*

semi-independent   hull-less   ultra-atomic   de-emphasize

(But: microorganism; cooperation; reenter)

14.08/15—A hyphen is ordinarily used with the prefixes *self-* and *all-*, the suffixes *-like* and *-type*, and with *ex-* (meaning "former") and *-elect* and *-designate* when joined to a title. Follow *Webster's International Dictionary.*

self-inflicted   self-respect   all-powerful

    tumor-like   Hopkins-type valve   the ex-mayor

    chairman-elect   AMA Executive Vice-President-Designate

14.08/16—In complex modifying phrases that include suffixes or prefixes, hyphens are sometimes used to avoid ambiguity.

    non-self-governing   non-group-specific blood

14.08/17—When two or more hyphenated compounds have a common base, omit the base in all but the last. In unhyphenated compounds written as one word, repeat the base.

    first-, second-, and third-stage tests

    10- and 15-year-old boys

    preoperative and postoperative therapy

    (*But not:* pre- and postoperative therapy.)

14.08/18—In expressing dimensions, use hyphens and spacing in accordance with the following examples. In the text, do not use hyphens to express ranges.

in a 10- to 14-day period	of 10 to 14 days' duration
a 3×4-cm strip	a strip measuring 3×4 cm
in 5% to 10% of the patients	in a range of 5% to 10%
a 5- to 10-μg dose	a dose of 5 to 10 μg
in a 5-, 10-, or 15-μg dose	a 5- to 10-mg dose
(Fig 4 through 6)	a dose of 5 to 10 mg
a 25-mg dose	a dose of 25 mg

14.08/19—Hyphenate compound cardinals and ordinals 21 through 99 when written out, as at the beginning of a sentence (**11.05**).

    Thirty-nine patients were examined.

    Twenty-first birthdays are often celebrated extravagantly.

    One hundred ninety-nine patients died.

14.08/20—Do not hyphenate a spelled-out common fraction used as a noun. (See **11.03/H**.)

Thomas reported the finding in two thirds of the patients studied.

(*But:* Each flask was two-thirds full.)

14.08/21—Compound designations of office are hyphenated as follows:

vice-president	secretary-treasurer
past vice-president	acting secretary
vice-chairman	honorary chairman
executive vice-president	past president

14.08/22—For correct division of a word at the end of a line (indicated by a hyphen), follow *Webster's International Dictionary.*

14.08/23—Special combinations may or may not necessitate use of hyphens. Consult *Dorland's, Stedman's,* and *Webster's International Dictionary.*

T wave	γ-globulin	I beam (is I-shaped)	
T-shirt	T square	*t* test	T tube

Parentheses—14.09

14.09/1—Use parentheses to indicate parenthetical explanation, identification, direction to the reader, or translation. (See also **14.02.**)

A known volume of air (100 cc) was injected.

The changes were not significant ($P > .10$).

One of us (B.O.G.) saw the patient in 1954.

One patient had severe thrombocytopenic purpura (Fig 5).

Asymmetry of the upper part of the rib cage (patient 11) and pseudoarthrosis of the first and second ribs (patient 6) were incidental anomalies (Table 2).

Three of our patients (No. 3, 7, and 8) had terminal cancer.

Of the 761 hospitalized patients, 171 (22.5%) were infants (under 2 years of age).

In this issue of *JAMA* (p 1037), a successful transplant is reported.

14.09/2—When the proper name of an institution, organization, or publication includes a place name, the state may be identified parenthetically, except in specific addresses. (See also **1.13.**)

Winter Park (Fla) Memorial Hospital

Springfield (Mass) Republican

When the proper name includes the name of a county, do not abbreviate state name (**1.11**).

Cook County (Illinois) Sanitary District

14.09/3—For enumerations, use parentheses in accordance with **11.15**.

14.09/4—Use parentheses to enclose all or part of a reference given in the text. (See also **15.02**.)

The case was originally reported in the *Archives of Surgery* (148:343-346, 1975).

The legality of this practice was questioned more than a decade ago (*Br Med J* 2:394-396, 1963).

14.09/5—In legends, use parentheses to identify a case or patient (**8.05**).

Fig 6.—Facial paralysis on right side (patient 3).

Fig 2.—Fracture of left femur (case 7).

The date, if given, is similarly enclosed (**8.06**).

Fig 2.—Fracture of left femur (case 7, Oct 23, 1969).

For photomicrographs, give magnification in parentheses, and stain if relevant (**8.04**).

Fig 3.—Marrow aspiration 14 weeks after transplantation (Wright stain, original magnification × 600).

14.09/6—In the address for reprint requests and reader correspondence, when there is more than one author, indicate in parentheses the author who can be reached at this address. (See also **6.07**.)

Reprint requests to 469 Prospect St, Peekskill, NY 10566 (Dr Smith).

14.09/7—A trademark of a drug, if mentioned by the author, is enclosed in parentheses immediately after first use of the nonproprietary name in the text and in the synopsis-abstract or summary. (See also **10.05/3**.)

Treatment included oral administration of phentolamine (Regitine) hydrochloride, 50 mg four times daily.

14.09/8—If used more than once in the text, specialized abbreviations as specified in **1.03** and those specifically indicated in section **1.22** are enclosed in parentheses immediately after first mention of the term, which is spelled out in full.

14.09/9—Explanatory footnotes may be incorporated into the text by means of parentheses.

Period—14.10

14.10/1—Use a period at the end of a declarative sentence, at the end of each footnote, legend, and after an indirect question not requiring an answer.

Surgery began at 9:15 AM.

Where, indeed, is the Osler of today.

Show us how you did it.

14.10/2—For enumeration of paragraphed items, use arabic numbers with periods. (See also **11.15**.)

14.10/3—Use the period as a decimal indicator. (See also **11.03/F**.)

$P < .01$ $r = .75$

$19.10 0.123%

.32 caliber $\pi = 3.14159$

14.10/4—Generally, the period should *not* be used in raised position to show multiplication.

Avoid: $4 \cdot 5 = 20$

Use: $4 \times 5 = 20$

14.10/5—A period is used after a run-in sidehead and numerical designations of Figures and Tables.

Diagnoses.—Each patient was seen within 24 hours of his first acute attack.

Fig 1.—Subcutaneous nodule (left elbow).

Table 2.—Patients With Polycythemia

14.10/6—Omit the period from titles, running feet, scientific and chemical symbols, abbreviations (**1.01, 1.21, 1.22**), and each line of a parallel series of sentence fragments, except the last.

Fe F test

H_2SO_4 Δt

14.10/7—The period precedes ending quotation marks and reference citations.

> *Quoth the Raven, "Nevermore."*

Question Mark—14.11

14.11/1—The question mark is used to end interrogative sentences or to show doubt on the part of the author for a specific datum.

> How much did the organ weigh?

> He was chief of staff for many years (21?).

> Catiline (108?-62 BC) lived during the time of Cato the Younger.

Quotation Marks—14.12

14.12/1—Use English quotation marks only.

14.12/2—Use quotation marks to enclose a direct quotation of no more than four typewritten lines.

14.12/3—Direct quotations of more than four typewritten lines are set as excerpts in reduced type, column width, without quotation marks. To indicate a quotation within copy that is already in reduced type, regardless of how long it is, use double quotation marks. A 4-point space should be added both above and below the quotation.

14.12/4—In all quoted material, follow the wording, spelling, and punctuation exactly. Whenever possible, verify the quotation from the original.

14.12/5—Use single quotation marks in titles.

> The 'Sense' of Humor

14.12/6—To indicate an omission in quoted material, use ellipses (**14.06/1**).

14.12/7—To indicate editorial interpolation in quoted material, use brackets (**14.02/1**). Use [*sic*] whenever the quotation contains an incorrect or apparently absurd statement.

14.12/8—Place closing quotation marks *outside* commas and periods, *inside* colons and semicolons. Place a question mark inside quotation marks *only when the quoted material is a question*.

> Why bother to do autopsies at all if the net result is invariably "edema and congestion of the viscera"?

> The clinician continues to ask, "Why did he die?"

14.12/9—Coined words, slang, and words or phrases used ironically or facetiously may be enclosed in quotation marks at first mention. Thereafter omit quotation marks.

This bone acts as the fulcrum or "nut" and thus causes the "flat-top" talus in the victim of the "nutcracker" treatment.

They called him a "square" because he preferred classical music to jazz.

It has been said that shoes and latrines are the best "medicine" for ancylostomiasis (hookworm disease).

14.12/10—The initial quotation mark should be omitted when an article beginning with a stand-up or drop two-line initial also begins with a quotation. It is, however, best to avoid this construction.

D octors need some patience," a sage has said.

14.12/11—Enclose in quotation marks a particular word or phrase that is mentioned rather than used, either (1) when the meaning might be unclear otherwise or (2) when the definition is given. (See also **20.02/2.**)

The word "logic" is often used loosely.

To some, "goodness" means excellence; to others, virtue.

14.12/12—Enclose in quotation marks a common word used in a technical sense when the context does not make the meaning clear.

In many publications, "running feet" face the "gutter" at the bottom of the page.

Both the subjects and the investigators in the first testing period were "blind."

14.12/13—In the text, use quotation marks to enclose titles of short poems, essays, radio and television programs, movies, songs, paintings, sculpture, parts of published works (chapters, articles in a periodical), and parts of the same article (eg, the "Results" section). (See also **20.02/1.**)

14.12/14—A word or phrase following *so-called* should not be enclosed in quotation marks.

Semicolon—14.13

14.13/1—Use a semicolon to separate independent clauses in a compound sentence when no connective word is used. (In most instances it is equally correct to use a period and make two sentences.)

The pupils reacted to light and accommodation; extraocular movements were normal.

One patient died 19 hours after eating the contaminated food; the other survived a brief illness.

If clauses are short and similar in form, use a comma.

I came, I saw, I conquered.

14.13/2—Use a semicolon between main clauses joined by a conjunctive adverb (eg, *then, however, thus, hence, indeed, yet*). (In most instances it is equally correct to make two sentences.)

This consideration is important in any research; yet, it is often overlooked.

The word is often used loosely; indeed, it is not easy to define.

There are adequate laws on the books of most states; however, strict enforcement is the exception rather than the rule.

14.13/3—For clarity, use semicolons between items in a complex enumeration within a sentence. (In a simple series with little or no punctuation within the items, use commas.) (See also **3.03**.)

Three new members of the committee are Norman Lewis, MD, St Joseph, Mo; Kenneth L. Dawson, PhD, LaJolla, Calif; and Ralph W. Warren, MD, Portland, Me.

(*But:* Three new members of the committee are Drs Lewis, Dawson, and Warren.)

Virgule—14.14

14.14/1—Use the virgule in a "per" construction only when (1) the construction involves units of measure (including time), *and* (2) at least one element includes a specific numerical quantity, *and* (3) the element immediately adjacent on each side is either a specific numerical quantity or a unit of measure. In such cases the units of measure should be abbreviated in accordance with **1.21**. (See also **11.04**.)

Hemoglobin level was 14 gm/100 ml.

Leukocyte count was 4,200/cu mm.

Ammonia in the urine measured 30 mEq/liter.

Blood volume was 80 ml/kg of body weight.

The drug was given in a dosage of 50 mg/day for three days.

The drug concentration was $16\mu g$/ml of serum.

Serum carotenoids measured 3 units/ml.

Respirations were 60/min.

(*But:* Pulse rate was 98 beats per minute.)

Do *not* use the virgule in a "per" construction (1) when a prepositional phrase intervenes between the two elements, (2) when neither
element contains a specific numerical quantity, or (3) in unusual expressions of a nontechnical nature.

4.5 mEq of potassium per milliliter

expressed in millimeters per minute

two days per year (*Better:* two days each year)

Do not use the virgule in dates, except in tables to save space (**18.03**).

14.14/2—The virgule is also used to set off phonemes and phonetic transcrip-
tion and to divide run-in lines of poetry.

/d/ as in *dog*

. . . cold-breathed earth/earth of the slumbering and liquid
trees/earth of the mountains misty-topped.

REFERENCES—15.00

15.01—**Listed References**—References to scientific publications are listed in
numerical order at the end of the communication (except as in **15.02**).
Each reference is a separate paragraphed entry.

References to nonscientific publications ordinarily are not acceptable
as listed references, except in unusual circumstances. Do not include in
listed references mass-circulation magazines and newspapers unless
special circumstances warrant such inclusion. (See **15.02**.)

15.02—**References Given in Text**—In some communications, references may be
included parenthetically in the text. Examples of correct forms are
given here. Note that in the text, (1) author(s) may or may not be
named, (2) title is not given, (3) name of journal is abbreviated only
when enclosed in parentheses, and (4) inclusive page numbers are
given.

The results were reported recently by Stern (*Br Med J* 1:665-667,
1968).

The results were reported recently in the *British Medical Journal*
(1:665-667, 1968).

References to publications not acceptable as listed references **(15.01)** may be included parenthetically in the text. Use a concise form: name of periodical, date, initial page number.

This explanation is given in one recent account (*Newsweek*, March 4, 1968, p 80).

15.03—**Accuracy and Verification**—The author is responsible for the accuracy and completeness of the references in his communication. References to the specific journal in which an article is to be published must be verified from the original; eg, in a *JAMA* manuscript all *JAMA* references must be checked for accuracy in the published issues. *Any* reference that appears to be inaccurate must be verified. Consult the bibliographic resources in the library or ask the author to verify and complete his references.

15.04—**Minimum Acceptable Data**—To be acceptable, a reference must include certain minimum data, as follows:

Journals—Author, article title, journal, volume, inclusive pages, year.

Books—Author, title, publication site, publisher, year.

Other Sources—Enough information must be provided so that the material can be identified and retrieved.

More complete data **(15.13, 15.26)** should be used when available.

15.05—**Number Permitted**—In *JAMA*, the number of references is generally limited to 20 in major contributions and fewer in shorter articles. Exceptions may be made if appropriate in the opinion of the reviewing editor.

15.06—**Numbering**—References should be numbered consecutively, in Arabic numerals, in the order they are cited in the text. Unnumbered references are not used in any AMA scientific journals.

15.07—**Citation**—Each reference should be cited in the text. Citation may also be made in tables, figures, and legends. Use Arabic superscript numerals. These numerals appear outside periods and commas, inside colons and semicolons. When more than two references are cited at a given place in the copy, use hyphens to join the first and last numbers of a closed series; use commas without space to separate other parts of a multiple citation.

As reported previously,[1,3-8,19]

The derived data were as follows[3-7]:

When a multiple citation involves more than 20 characters, use an asterisk in the text and give the citation in a footnote at the bottom of the page. Note that reference numerals in such a footnote are set full-size on-line rather than as superscripts.

*References 3, 5, 7, 9, 11, 13, 21, 24-29.

If the author wishes to cite different page numbers from a single reference source at different places in the text, the page numbers are included in the superscript citation and the source appears only once in the list of references. Note that (1) the superscript may include more than one page number, citation of more than one reference, or both, and (2) all spaces are closed up.

> These patients showed no sign of protective sphincteric adduction.[5(p21),9]

> Westman has reported eight cases in which vomiting occurred.[5(pp3,5),9]

Note: In listed references, do not use *ibid*, or *op cit*. Do not repeat the source.

15.08—**Authors**—Use the surname followed by initials without punctuation. In listed references, the names of all authors should be given unless there are more than three, in which case the names of the *first three authors are used, followed by "et al."* Correct forms are given here. Note spacing and minimum punctuation. Do not use "and" between names. (Abbreviation for *junior* or *senior* follows author's initials.)

> *One author*—Doe JF:

> *Two authors*—Doe JF, Roe JP:

> *Three authors*—Doe JF, Roe JP, Loe JT Jr:

> *Four or more*—Doe JF, Roe JP, Loe JT Jr, et al:

When mentioned in the text, only surnames of authors are used. For a two-author reference, give both surnames. For references with more than two authors, use the first author's surname followed by "et al," "and associates," "and others," "and co-workers," or "and colleagues."

> Doe[7] reported on the survey.

> Doe and Roe[8] reported on the survey.

> Doe et al[9] reported on the survey.

(*NB*—Never use the possessive form *et al's*; rephrase sentence.)

> The data of Doe et al were reported.

REFERENCES

15.09—Prefixes and Particles—Surnames containing particles or prefixes should be spelled and alphabetized according to the personal preference of the persons concerned, except for the first author's name, where the particle is always capitalized.

  1. Van Gylswyk NO, Roche CE:

  2. DePhillips HA Jr, Nickerson KW, van Gylswyk NO:

15.10—Titles—In titles of articles, books, parts of books, and other material, retain the spelling and abbreviations of the original, but follow AMA style for numbers **(11.00)**. Note, however, that *all* numbers are spelled out at the beginning of a title.

Articles and parts of books: In English-language titles, capitalize only the first letter of the first word, proper names, and abbreviations that are ordinarily capped (eg, DNA, EEG, VDRL). Do *not* enclose parts of books in quotation marks.

Books; government bulletins, documents, and journals; and pamphlets: In English-language titles, capitalize the first and last word and each word that is not an article, preposition, or conjunction of less than four letters. In every language, italicize the title.

Genus and species: In all titles, follow AMA style for capitalization of genera and species and use of italics **(4.16, 10.07/3, 10.07/4)**. Do not italicize genus and species names in book titles.

15.11—Foreign-Language Titles—Foreign-language titles are usually not translated; if they have been, parenthetical indication of the original language should follow the title. They should be verified from the original when possible. Consult foreign-language dictionaries or persons in the Abstracting Department for accents, spelling, and other particulars.

Capitalization: For journal articles, follow the capitalization in *Index Medicus*. For books, pamphlets, and parts of books, retain the capitalization used in the original or consult the Abstracting Department. *Note:* In foreign-language titles, capitalization does not necessarily follow the rules given in **15.10**. For example, in German titles (both articles and books), all nouns and only nouns are capitalized; in French, Spanish, and Italian book titles, capitalize only the first word, proper names, and abbreviations that are ordinarily capitalized.

15.12—Subtitles—Style for subtitles follows that for titles **(15.10)** in regard to spelling, abbreviations, numbers, capitalization, and use of italics. A colon separates title and subtitle. If the subtitle is numbered, use a Roman numeral followed by a period.

  1. Rifind D: Infectious diseases associated with renal homotransplantation: I. Incidence, types, and predisposing factors *JAMA* 189:397-401, 1964.

REFERENCES

References to Journals

15.13—**Complete Data**—A complete journal reference includes (1) authors' names and initials; (2) title of article, and subtitle if any; (3) abbreviated name of journal; (4) volume number; (5) inclusive page numbers; (6) year; and (7) part or supplement number, when pertinent, and issue month or number when pagination is not consecutive throughout a volume.

15.14—**Names of Journals**—Abbreviate and italicize names of journals. Use initial capitals. Abbreviate according to the listing in the current *Index Medicus*, but do not include parenthetical designation of a city. In journal titles listed in *Index Medicus*, information enclosed in brackets should be omitted.

If the name of a journal has changed, use the name current when the reference was published, but abbreviate it according to the current *Index Medicus*. The changing names and correct abbreviations for one AMA specialty journal are given here as examples:

Archives of Dermatology & Syphilology [1920-1950]
A.M.A. Archives of Dermatology & Syphilology [1951-1955]
  Arch Dermatol Syphilol

A.M.A. Archives of Dermatology [1955-1960]
Archives of Dermatology [1960-19——]
  Arch Dermatol

15.15—**Page Numbers and Dates**—When inclusive page numbers are given, do not omit digits. The volume number, the colon following it, and the page numbers are set close.

> 1. Wiechemann E: Difficulties in diagnosis during insulin coma. *JAMA* 92:1495-1496, 1929.

15.16—**Serialized Article**—For a serialized article, the cited parts of which appear in the same volume, follow this example:

> 1. Lerner PI, Weinstein L: Infective endocarditis in the antibiotic era. *N Engl J Med* 274:199-206, 388-393, 1966.

15.17—**Journals Without Volume Numbers**—In references to journals that have no volume numbers, use the following style:

> 1. Legrand MJ: Les manifestations oculaires du virus herpetique. *Bull Soc Ophtalmol Fr*, 1959, pp 653-677.

> 2. Hunter TH, Paterson PY: Bacterial endocarditis. *DM*, November 1956.

3. Orringer MB, Kirsh MM, Sloan H: Congenital and traumatic diaphragmatic hernias exclusive of the hiatus. *Curr Probl Surg,* March 1975, pp 1-64.

15.18—**Parts of a Volume**—If a volume has two or more parts, the part cited should be indicated in accordance with the following example:

1. Glomm RP: Hypertension. *Arch Dis Heart* 27(pt 1):214, 1958.

15.19—**Issue Number**—Do not include the issue number or month except in the case of a special issue (**15.20**) or when pagination is not consecutive throughout the volume. In the latter case, the month or date of the issue is preferable to the issue number.

Psychiatr Opinion 10:34-38, October 1973.

15.20—**Special Issues**—References to an entire special issue of a journal should be given as follows:

1. Francis T Jr: Evaluation of 1954 poliomyelitis vaccine trials: Summary report. *Am J Public Health* (special issue), vol 45, May (pt 2) 1955.

Note that month and part may be needed for identification.

The following example shows the pagination in a supplementary special issue.

2. Guidelines for the detection, diagnosis and management of hypertensive populations, Hypertension Study Group of the Intersociety Commission for Heart Disease Resources. *Circulation* 44:A263-A272, 1971.

15.21—**Supplements**—Two forms are used: (1) for journals with volume numbers, (2) for journals without volume numbers.

1. McCarthy PO: Allied medical education. *JAMA* 231(suppl):70-84, 1975.

(Use this form whether pagination is consecutive with volume pagination or not and whether this is the only supplement to the volume or if there are others.)

2. Johnston LD: Drug use during and after high school: Results of a national longitudinal study. *Am J Public Health* 64(December suppl):29-37, 1974.

(Pagination is not consecutive with that of the volume; there may be several supplements to a volume, referred to by month.)

3. Myrhed M: Alcohol consumption in relation to factors associated with ischemic heart disease: A co-twin control study. *Acta Med Scand,* suppl 567, 1974, pp 8-92.

(Supplements are published independently of volumes and are numbered; pagination in each is independent of others.)

4. Flodmark S: Clinical detection of blood-brain barrier alteration by means of EEG: Part I. *Acta Neurol Scand* 41(suppl 13, pt 1):163-177, 1965.

(Volume 41 has multiple supplements; this supplement has two parts, each with independent pagination.)

5. Health information for international travel: Including United States designated yellow fever vaccination centers. *Morbidity Mortality Weekly Rep* 23(September suppl):1-76, 1974.

(This refers to the supplement for September, although there is an annual supplement to the volume as well.)

6. Vaccination certificate requirements for international travel. *Morbidity Mortality Weekly Rep* 22(suppl to No. 17):1-54, 1973.

(This is a supplement to No. 17, although there are both monthly and annual supplements as well.)

15.22—**Abstracts**—Reference to an abstract of an article should be permitted only when the original article is not readily available (eg, foreign language articles or papers presented at meetings but not yet published). If possible, references for both the original article and the abstract should be given. If the abstract is in the society proceedings section of a journal, the name of the society before which the paper was read need not be included unless the subjects of paper, society, and journal are widely divergent.

1. Uthegenannt H, Stromlid A, Zwad HD: Radiological investigation of esophagus with scopolamine butylbromide hypotonia. *Fortschr Geb Roentgenstr Nuklearmed* 119:10-16, July 1973. Abstracted, *JAMA* 226:491, 1973.

2. Kerby GP: Occurrence of acid mucopolysaccharides in human leukocytes, abstracted. *J Clin Invest* 34:944, 1955.

15.23—**Special Department of a Journal**—When reference is made to material from a special department in a journal, the department should be identified only if the cited material has no by-line or signature.

Observe the following forms for capitalization: (1) For *JAMA* and AMA specialty journals, use small caps for the names of departments. (2) For other journals, use initial caps when the exact name of the department is given. Translate unusual names into general terms and use no caps, eg, change "Leading Articles" (*Br Med J*) to "editorials." (3) For all journals, use lowercase to identify editorials.

REFERENCES

1. Oral poliovirus vaccines, COUNCIL ON DRUGS. *JAMA* 197:1015-1016, 1964.

2. Welfare of fatherless families, medical news. *Br Med J* 2:132-133, 1964.

3. Drugs and Down syndrome, news. *Am J Public Health* 54:1034, 1964.

4. Suicide in the aging, editorial. *JAMA* 188:996, 1965.

5. Isocyanates in industry, editorial. *Lancet* 1:1375-1376, 1970.

6. Case 44201, Case records of the Massachusetts General Hospital: Weekly clinicopathologic exercises. *N Engl J Med* 258:1004-1008, 1958.

7. Krill AE (reviewer), Gass JDM: *Stereoscopic Atlas of Macular Diseases*, book review. *Trans Am Acad Ophthalmol Otolaryngol* 75:664-665, 1971.

15.24—Other Material Without Author(s)—Reference may be made to material that has no author or is authored by a committee or other group. The following forms are used:

1. Institutional outbreak of pneumonia. *Morbidity Mortality Weekly Rep* 14:265-266, 1965.

2. Expert Committee on Rabies: Sixth report. *WHO Tech Rep Ser* 523:5-55, 1973.

3. Multiple myeloma: General aspects of diagnosis, course, and survival. Study Committee of the Midwest Cooperative Chemotherapy Group. *JAMA* 188:741-745, 1964.

4. Effects of treatment on morbidity and hypertension: II. Results in patients with diastolic blood pressures averaging 90 through 114 mm Hg. Veterans Administration Group on Antihypertensive Agents. *JAMA* 213:1143-1152, 1970.

5. Insect-sting allergy: Questionnaire study of 2,606 cases, Insect Allergy Committee of the American Academy of Allergy. *JAMA* 193:115-120, 1965.

But note: In *JAMA*, reference to a report of an AMA committee, council, or department, with department heading, without by-line, should be edited in accordance with **15.23**.

15.25—Discussants—If reference citation in the text names a discussant specifically rather than the author(s), eg, "as noted by Sachs,[4]" the following form is used (See also **15.40**.):

1. Sachs W, in discussion, Baer RL, Andrade R, Selmanowitz VJ: Pemphigus erythematosus. *Arch Dermatol* 93:374-375, 1966.

References to Books

15.26—**Complete Data**—A complete reference to a book includes (1) authors' surnames and initials; (2) title of book and subtitle, if any; (3) number of edition after the first; (4) surname and initials of editor or translator or both, if any; (5) place of publication; (6) name of publisher; (7) year of publication; (8) volume number, if there is more than one; (9) page numbers if specific pages are cited.

1. Fisher RA: *Statistical Methods for Research Workers*, ed 11. London, Oliver & Boyd, 1950, pp 98-101.

2. Winawar S, Lipkin M: Proliferative abnormalities in the gastrointestinal tract, in Card WI, Creamer B (eds): *Modern Trends in Gastroenterology*, ed 4. London, Butterworth & Co, 1970, p 65.

15.27—**Publishers**—The full name of the publisher should be given, abbreviated in accordance with AMA style, but *without* punctuation. If the name of a publishing firm has changed, use the name that was current when the cited reference was published.

To verify names of publishers, consult *Books in Print*, the current issue of *Cumulative Book Index*, and *Publisher's Trade List Annual*.

Holt Rinehart & Winston Inc | Little Brown & Co

Henry Holt & Co Inc | Charles C Thomas Publisher

Harper & Row Publishers Inc | Harper & Bros

15.28—**Place of Publication**—Use the name of the city in which the publishing firm is located. Follow AMA style in the use of state names (**1.12**). A comma separates place of publication and name of publisher.

1. Cousteau JY: *Silent World*. New York, Harper & Bros, 1953.

15.29—**Page, Volume, and Edition Numbers**—Use Arabic numerals. Give specific page or pages if indicated by the author. The volume should be given if the work cited includes more than one volume. Do not indicate a first edition; if there have been subsequent editions, the number should be given. (See also **11.13**.)

1. Peer LA: *Transplantation of Tissues*. Baltimore, Williams & Wilkins Co, 1955, vol 1, p 148.

2. Fishbein M: *Medical Writing: Technic and Art*, ed 2. Philadelphia, Blakiston Co, 1950, pp 45-48.

3. AMA Department of Drugs: *AMA Drug Evaluations*, ed 2. Acton, Mass, Publishing Sciences Group, Inc, 1973.

REFERENCES

15.30—**Editors and Translators**—Names of editors, translators, translator-editors or executive and section editors are given in accordance with the following forms:

1. Osler W: *Modern Medicine,* ed 3, Lee DH (ed). Philadelphia, Lea & Febiger, 1927, vol 5, p 66.

2. Revere P: *Anatomy of the Lymphatic System,* Tobias MJ (trans-ed). Ann Arbor, Mich, Edwards Bros Inc, 1940.

3. Majno G: Ultrastructure of the vascular membrane, in Dow P (exec ed): *Handbook of Physiology: A Critical Comprehensive Presentation of Physiologic Knowledge and Concepts.* Section 2: *Circulation,* vol 3; WF Hamilton (section ed). Baltimore, Williams & Wilkins Co, 1965, pp 2293-2325.

(Handbook series for which there are executive and section editors and in which sections are composed of several volumes.)

4. Francis T Jr: *Factors Conditioning Resistance to Epidemic Influenza.* Harvey lectures 1941-1942. Lancaster, Pa, Science Press Printing Co, 1942, vol 37, pp 69-99.

(Serial publication with changing title, range of years of lecture, publication date, volume and changing pages.)

If a book has an editor or editors but no author(s), the following form is used:

1. Barach AL, Bickerman HA (eds): *Pulmonary Emphysema.* Baltimore, Williams & Wilkins Co, 1956.

2. Boyer PD, Lardy H, Myback K (eds): *Enzymes,* ed 2. New York, Academic Press Inc, 1959, vol 1, p 141.

But: When a book title includes a volume number, follow this example:

1. Davies CN (ed): *Inhaled Particles and Vapours, II.* Oxford, England, Pergamon Press, 1967.

15.31—**Parts of Books**—In some instances, reference is made to a part of a book that has a number of contributors as well as major authors or editors. In the title of the part (chapter or section), capitalize as for a journal article **(15.10)**; do *not* enclose in quotation marks. Either inclusive page numbers or numerical designation of the part should be given, but not both.

1. Mandell GL: Bacterial endocarditis, in Conn HF (ed): *Current Therapy.* Philadelphia, WB Saunders Co, 1971, pp 168-170.

2. Fullerton HW: Disorders of the blood, in Dunlop D, Alstead S, Macgregor AG (eds): *Textbook of Medical Treatment,* ed 11. Edinburgh, E & S Livingstone Ltd, 1968, pp 144-184.

REFERENCES

3. Keeder CS: Sulfonamides and antibiotics, in Smith A (ed): *Modern Treatment: A Guide for General Practice.* New York, Paul B Hoeber Inc, 1953, chap 4.

Special Materials

15.32—**Government Bulletins**—References to bulletins published by departments or agencies of the US government should include the following information, in the order indicated: (1) name of author, if given; (2) title of bulletin; (3) number of bulletin, or similar identification, if any; (4) place of publication except if it is Washington, DC; (5) name of issuing bureau, agency, department, or other governmental division; (6) date; (7) page numbers, if specified.

1. Hoffman FL: *Problem of Dust Phthisis in Granite-Stone Industry,* bulletin 293. US Dept of Labor, Bureau of Labor Statistics, 1922.

2. Hartwell JL: *Survey of Compounds Which Have Been Tested for Carcinogenic Activity.* Federal Security Agency, Public Health Service, 1941.

3. Marinell LD, Hill RF: Studies in dosage in cancer therapy, Brookhaven conference report, in *Symposium on Radioiodine,* unclassified document AECU, BNL—C-5. Oak Ridge, Tenn, Atomic Energy Commission, Technical Information Branch, 1949, p 98.

4. *Blood Pressure of Adults by Race and Area, United States, 1960-1962.* National Health Survey, Vital and Health Statistics Series II, No. 5. US Department of Health, Education and Welfare, Public Health Service, 1964.

5. *Peanuts and Tea. A Selected Glossary of Terms Used by Drug Addicts.* Lexington, Ky, National Institute of Mental Health Clinical Research Center, 1972.

15.33—**Serial Publications**—If a monograph or report is one of a series, include the name of the series and the number of the publication.

1. Pulaski EJ: *Surgical Infections: Prophylaxis-Treatment-Antibiotic Therapy,* publication 170. American Lecture Series, monograph in Bannerstone Division of American Lectures in Surgery, New York, McGraw-Hill Book Co Inc, 1961.

2. Rappaport H: *Tumors of the Hematopoietic System.* Atlas of Tumor Pathology, Armed Forces Institute of Pathology, 1966, section 3, pt 8, pp 36-60.

15.34—**Theses**—Titles are given in italics. References to English or American theses should include the name of the university (or other institution), its location, and, if it has been published, the publisher.

For foreign theses, the city of publication is sufficient.

1. Pollock BE: *Effect of Carbon Arc Radiation on Cardiac Output in Dogs,* thesis. Tulane University Graduate School, New Orleans, 1953.

2. Merle P: *Études sur les épendymites cérébrales,* thesis, Paris, 1910.

15.35—Special Collections—References to materials available only in special collections of a library take this form:

1. Hunter J: An account of the dissection of morbid bodies: A monograph or lecture: No. 32, 1757, pp 30-32 (available in Library of Royal College of Surgeons, London).

15.36—Congressional Record and Federal Register—References to the *Congressional Record* and *Federal Register* take these forms:

1. Bregan PR: The return of lobotomy and psychosurgery. *Congressional Record* 118:E1602-E1612 (Feb 24) 1972.

2. Notice of proposed rule-making on incentive grant criteria for state safety belt use laws. *Federal Register* 38:32818-32819 (Nov 28) 1973.

3. Federal Motor Vehicle Safety Standard 213, Child seating systems. *Federal Register* 35:5120 (March 26) 1970; amended 35:14778 (Sept 23) 1970, 36:6895-6896 (April 10) 1971, 36:12224-12226 (June 29) 1971, 38:7562 (March 23) 1973.

4. Incentive grant criteria for state safety belt use laws (23 CFR 1213). *Federal Register* 39:13154 (April 11) 1974.

5. Notice of proposed rulemaking on Federal Motor Vehicle Safety Standard 213, Child seating systems. *Federal Register* 39:7959-7960 (March 1) 1974.

15.37—Statutory Publications—Occasionally, need arises to cite a Congressional Act. The form for citation is as follows:

1. *The Allied Health Professions Personnel Training Act of 1966,* 42 USC, 295h.

15.38—Audiotapes, Videotapes—Occasionally, references may include citation of audiotapes or videotapes. The form for such references is as follows:

1. *Food From the Sea: The Hunting Stage,* monaural tape, series 65, The Ocean Depths: A New Frontier. Baltimore, Smith & Sons, 1962.

2. *Pica and Elite,* videotape produced by the City School District

of Rochester, NY. Distributed by New York State Education Department, Albany, NY, 1968.'

3. *Program 6—Digitalis II: Clinical Pharmacology of Digoxin*, audiotape. Bethesda, Md, American College of Cardiology Extended Learning, 1973.

15.39—**Unpublished Material**—References to unpublished material may include (1) articles that have been read before a society but not published and (2) material accepted for publication but not published. Date of publication and additional data should be added when they become known.

1. Reinarz JA: Percutaneous lung aspiration: A useful diagnostic adjunct in pneumonia. Read before the Ninth Interscience Conference on Antimicrobial Agents and Chemotherapy, Atlantic City, NJ, Oct 19, 1974.

2. Kornetsky CH: Psychological effects of chronic barbiturate intoxication. *Arch Neurol,* to be published.

In the list of references, do not include material that has been submitted for publication but is not yet accepted. This material, with its date, should be noted in the text as "unpublished data," as follows:

These findings have recently been corroborated (H. E. Marman, MD, unpublished data, January 1975).

Similar findings have been noted by Roberts[6] and by H. E. Marman, MD (unpublished data, February 1974).

Do not include "personal communications" in the list of references. The following forms may be used:

In a conversation with H. E. Marman, MD (August 1966) . . .

According to a letter from H. E. Marman, MD, in August 1966 . . .

Similar findings have been noted by Roberts[6] and by H. E. Marman, MD (written communication, August 1966).

Note that the author should give the date of the communication and indicate whether it was in conversation or in writing. Highest academic degrees should also be given.

15.40—**Secondary Citations and Quotations**—Reference may be made to one author's citation of, or quotation from, another's work. Distinguish between citation and quotation, ie, between work mentioned and words actually quoted. In the text, the name of the original author should be mentioned rather than the secondary source. (See also **15.25**.) The forms for listed references are as follows:

REFERENCES

1.   Hooper PJ, cited by Wilson CB, Cronic F: Traumatic arteriovenous fistulas involving middle meningeal vessels. *JAMA* 188:953-957, 1964.

2.   Mitchell J, quoted by Goodfield GJ: *Growth of Scientific Physiology.* New York, Dover Publications Inc, 1960, p 89.

15.41—Classical References—These may deviate from the usual forms in some details. In many instances, the facts of publication are irrelevant and may be omitted. Date of publication should be given when available and pertinent.

1.   Shakespeare W: *Midsummer Night's Dream,* Act II, scene 3, line 24.

2.   Donne J: *Second Anniversary,* verse 243.

For some classical references, the University of Chicago's *A Manual of Style* may be used as a guide, but use a colon after an author's name.

3.   Aristotle: *Metaphysics* 3. 2.996^b 5-8.

In biblical references, do not abbreviate names of books. The version may be included parenthetically if the information is provided. References to the Bible are usually included in the text but may occasionally appear as listed references at the end of the paper.

The story begins in Genesis 3:28.

Paul admonished against temptation (I Corinthians 10:6-13).

4.   I Corinthians 10:6-13 (RSV).

15.42—Legal References—A specific style variation is used for references to legal citations. In its simplest form, a legal reference includes, in this order, (1) the name of the case; (2) the volume number; (3) abbreviated identification of the record, ie, state, area, federal; (4) the page number; and (5) the year.

In addition, documentation may include designation of a supplement (Suppl) as well as a series number (2d—do not change to 2nd). Reference may also be made to state, area, federal, and court records in various combinations.

15.42/1—Citation of Cases—Follow the style in the examples given. Note that (1) name of the case is italicized, (2) *vs* is used as abbreviation for versus, and (3) all abbreviations are used without periods.

1.   *Fellner vs Maryland Bar Association,* 131 A 2d 729, 1957.

2.   *Perlmutter vs Beth David Hospital,* 308 NY 100, 123 NE 2d 792, 1954.

3. *Necolayfe vs Genessee Hospital*, 270 App Div 648, 61 NYS 2d 832, 1946.

4. *Legare vs United States*, 195 F Suppl 557 (SD, Fla, 1961).

15.42/2—Slip Law

1. *National Environmental Policy Act of 1969*, Public Law 91-190. US Congress, Senate, 91st Congress, first session, Jan 1, 1970.

15.42/3—Codified Law

1. *Environmental Quality Improvement Act of 1970*, 43 USCA, 4372.

15.42/4—Presidential Documents

1. Nixon RM: Protection and enhancement of environmental quality, Executive Order 11514, in *Weekly Compilation of Presidential Documents*. Office of the Federal Register, March 9, 1970, vol 6, No. 10, pp 320-321.

15.42/5—Testimony

1. *Testimony of William Stewart, MD, Surgeon General, Public Health Service: Hearings Before the Consumer Subcommittee of the Committee on Commerce*. US Senate, 90th Congress, first session, Aug 25, 1967.

A legal reference may be included in the text, either (1) in full or (2) in part, with full documentation given in the listed references.

in a recent decision (*Ericksen vs Wilson*, 123 NW 2d 687, 1964)

in a recent decision[9]

in the case of *Lawless vs Calaway* (147 P 2d 604, 1974)

in the case of *Lawless vs Calaway*[9]

15.43—**Foreign Words of Reference**—Such words as *tome* (volume), *fascicolo* (part), *Seite* (page), *Teil* (part), *Auflage* (edition), *Abteilung* (section or part), *Band* (volume), *Heft* (number), *Beiheft* (supplement), and *Lieferung* (part or number) should be translated.

RUNNING FEET/HEADS—16.00

Printed pages customarily carry identification of the publication (ie, journal name or abbreviation, volume number, date of issue), the article (by truncated title) and author(s) (surnames), and the page number (also called the *folio*). The information in AMA scientific publications usually appears at the bottom of the page. The line giving the truncated title and author identification (or section title alone, where applicable) is called the "running foot."

16.01—The running foot should usually be of fewer than 45 characters and spaces, should identify the article or section beginning or continuing on the page, and give the surname of the author. For a two-author article, give both surnames joined by an ampersand. For articles having three or more authors, use the surname of the first followed by "et al." Separate the truncated title from the name(s) of the author(s) by an em dash. No punctuation follows the running foot.

Emergency Medical Service Systems—Harvey

Miconazole Therapy—Hoeprich & Goldstein

Herpesvirus Infection—Arora et al

16.02—In special circumstances, an identification may be needed in addition to the running feet for contents of successive pages. Use of running heads should be considered in such cases. (For an example, see the *Continuing Education Courses for Physicians* supplement to *JAMA* published Aug 11, 1975.)

16.03—The following abbreviations will be used to identify AMA journals in running feet.

Am J Dis Child	Arch Neurol
Arch Dermatol	Arch Ophthalmol
Arch Gen Psychiatry	Arch Otolaryngol
Arch Intern Med	Arch Pathol

Arch Surg

STATISTICS—17.00

17.01—These standard forms should be used for statistical symbols.

$\| \|$	absolute difference
χ^2	chi-square, symbol for comparison of obtained deviations with expected deviations
r	correlation test symbol
df	degrees of freedom

STATISTICS

n!	(n) factorial
f	frequency
$\bar{X}$,M	mean of population
$\bar{x}$,m	mean of sample
$\bar{\bar{X}}$	weighted mean
median	Do not abbreviate.
mode	Do not abbreviate.
N	number in population
n	number in sample
P	probability
X	raw score, population data
x	raw score, sample data
σ, SD	standard deviation
Σ	sum (summation)
SE	standard error
SEM	standard error of the mean
type I	error designation, rejecting null hypothesis erroneously
type II	error designation, accepting null hypothesis erroneously
σ^2	variance, population
s^2	variance, sample
F	variance ratio symbol
t	Student distribution symbol
z	standard score, standard normal variate
D	difference
$\bar{D}$	mean difference

TABLES—18.00

18.01—The purpose of tabulation is to present data more vividly and concisely than is possible in the text. Tables can often be condensed: a factor common to all elements in a column can be incorporated into a column heading; a variable pertaining to only one or a few entries in a large series can be indicated in a footnote (Table 1).

A single column of data or listing is not considered to be a table per se. Occasionally, however, circumstances may require tabular presentation (Table 2).

18.02—Table titles should be brief. Articles (*a, an, the*) and phrases such as "summary of," "findings in," "evaluation of," "number of" can usually be omitted. Explanation, if needed, may be given in a footnote. Tables in an article are numbered sequentially and all must be cited in the text. If it is the only table in a communication, its caption should contain only the title.

18.03—Abbreviations, numerals, and symbols are used extensively in tables to save space. Use standard abbreviations (**1.21, 1.22**) when they exist; explain unusual or specialized abbreviations in footnotes.

In table titles and footnotes, use numerals as specified in **11.00**. In column heads and text of the table, use numerals throughout.

To express range in tables, use hyphens.

> 4-8 mo   5-10 wk   1956-1963

In dates, use virgules, numerals for month, and two digits for the year.

> 5/26/69

18.04—For table titles and column heads, follow style for article titles (**19.00**).

In stubs (first entry in horizontal columns) and their subdivisions, capitalize only the first word (Table 1).

In column heads and stubs, separate units of measure from descriptors by commas (Tables 3 and 4).

18.05—Use zeros to indicate "none" in answer to the implied question "how much?" or "how many?" (Table 1).

Use ellipses to indicate that no data were available or that a specified category of data is not applicable. (Table 1) (See also **14.06/2**.)

If all entries in any one column are expressed in decimal fractions less than one, zeros must be used before the cipher. Decimal points should be aligned.

TABLES

18.06—Data in tables must agree with any comment thereon in the text of the communication. Totals and percentages must be checked for accuracy. When percentages are given in a series that includes fewer than 100 subjects, the actual numbers should also be given (Table 5). When the data add up to fewer than 100 entries, the percentages should be rounded to the nearest whole number. If the data add up to between 100 and 1,000 units, the percentages should be rounded to the nearest tenth. (See also **12.00.**)

18.07—Totals and subtotals should be in boldface (Table 5).

18.08—**Footnote Symbols**—Numerals are used to indicate bibliographical references only (Table 1).

In tables (and in rare instances in the text), explanatory footnotes are indicated by the following symbols, used in the order shown: * (asterisk), † (dagger), ‡ (double dagger), § (section mark), || (parallels), ¶ (paragraph mark), # (number sign), and doubling of these symbols if more are needed. Symbols appear after commas and periods, before colons and semicolons.

18.09—Use full-table-width hairline rules to delineate information for individual stubs.

18.10—Runover lines for stubs or column entries should be indented and hung (Table 4). Column heads are centered and stacked over the columns (Tables 1 and 3).

18.11—To cite a bibliographical reference, the appropriate superscript numeral may be inserted in the text of the table (Table 1) or the following form used as footnote to the table:

*Data from Daufman and Berstein.[3]

Note that the reference should only be cited, not given in full. The complete reference should appear in the list of references, numbered either according to the citation of the table in the text, or with the table considered as end material (Tables 1 and 6).

18.12—To reproduce a table that has been used previously, the author must have written permission from the publisher. The source should be acknowledged either (1) in a footnote to the table or (2) in an acknowledgment footnote at the end of the communication (**6.08**).

Table 2.—Incidence of Thromboembolic Complications*

---

*From James.[10]

Table 2 is reproduced with permission from *Lancet* (2:459-465, 1960).

18.13—Tables in LETTERS or other special departments may be printed without titles.

Table 1.—Common Manifestations of Colorectal Cancer				
	Occurrence, %			
Manifestation	Cattell et al[19] (148 Cases)	Hallstrand[20] (252 Cases)	Palumbo et al[21] (80 Cases)	DePeyster and Gilchrist[3] (100 Cases)
Change in bowel habits	69.3	...	72.55	50.0
Pain	68.0	69.96	81.25	24.0
Blood in stool (gross)	66.0	66.40	48.75	47.0
Anemia	20.6	4.35	0.0	12.0
Palpable mass (abdominal)	13.3	25.00	35.20	10.0
Weight loss	50.6	76.28	66.25	6.0*
Obstruction	0	10.27	25.00	10.0
Asymptomatic	0	0	...	7.0

*Weight loss exceeding 4.5 kg (10 lb) within six months before treatment.

Table 2.—Classification of Polyps of the Colon and Rectum
Nonneoplastic
Inflammatory
Inflammatory polyp
Pseudopolyposis
Colitis cystica profunda
Lymphoid polyps and polyposis
Growth anomalies
Retention (juvenile)
Juvenile polyposis (familial)
Peutz-Jegher polyposis
Hyperplastic
Hyperplastic (metaplastic)
Neoplastic
Carcinoid
Leiomyoma

Time, Weeks	Serum Calcium, mg/100 ml	Urinary Calcium Excretion, mg/24 hr	Serum Phosphorus, mg/100 ml	Urinary Phosphorus Excretion, mg/24 hr
Patient 1				
0	8.0	38	12.0	457
1	8.7	58	5.9	292
2	10.4	83	4.6	128
3	10.8	90	2.9	117
4	10.6	92	2.8	112
Patient 2				
0	8.4	42	6.3	380
1	8.8	62	4.6	143
2	9.5	60	2.8	72
3	10.5	83	2.5	40
4	10.4	92	2.6	45

Table 3.—Serum Concentrations and Daily Urinary Excretion Rates of Calcium and Phosphorus

Table 4.—Biochemical Findings

| | Patient | | | | | |
| | 1 | | 2 | | 3 | |
	Initial	End	Initial	End	Initial	End
Inulin clearance, ml/min	6.2	5.8	9.1	8.2	5.2	4.6
Serum parathyroid hormone, pg/ml (normal, 90-420)	2,210	250	9,230	290	980	165
Serum phosphorus, mg/100 ml	12.0	3.2	6.3	2.8	10.2	3.1
Serum calcium mg/100 ml	8.0	10.2	8.4	10.6	7.9	10.0

Table 5.—Death Related to Number of Days in Hospital		
Day	**No. (%) Untreated**	**No. (%) Treated**
0	4 (7.1)	2 (4.2)
1	3 (5.4)	1 (2.1)
2	5 (8.9)	3 (6.3)
3	6 (10.7)	11 (22.9)
4	2 (3.6)	3 (6.3)
5	2 (3.6)	4 (8.3)
6	2 (3.6)	2 (4.2)
7	3 (5.4)	0
8-14	17 (30.4)	11 (22.9)
15-21	7 (12.5)	8 (16.7)
>21	5 (8.9)	3 (6.3)
Total	**56 (100)**	**48 (100)**

Table 6.—Distribution of Grades of Malignancy*						
				%		
Source, yr	**Total Cases**	**Grade 1**	**Grade 2**	**Grade 3**	**Grade 4**	**Colloid**
Rankin and Broders,[15] 1928	598	17.6	50.0	23.5	8.9	...
Dukes,[16] 1937	600	6.0	54.0	26.0	2.0	12.0
Broders et al,[17] 1940	432	16.9	55.8	23.1	4.2	...
Broders,[18] 1940	580	14.6	51.8	24.5	9.1	...
Broders et al,[13] 1952	667	29.3	47.1	21.2	2.2	...

*Grade 1 malignancy includes lesions in which 100% to 75% of the cells are differentiated; grade 2, from 75% to 50%; grade 3, from 50% to 25%; and grade 4, from 25% to 0%.

TITLES, SUBTITLES—19.00

This section provides style guidelines for titles and subtitles of scientific articles and of editorials, letters to the editor, questions and answers, and other subsidiary copy.

19.01—**Titles**—Titles are subject to editing in accordance with style and layout requirements. Any modification of a title should be called to the author's attention. Major revision of a title should be approved by the senior editor-reviewer (*JAMA*) or editor-consultant (specialty journals).

19.02—The title of a manuscript should be concise, informative, and clear. Phrases such as "The Use of," "Effect of," "A Report of" can usually be omitted.

A subtitle may be used to amplify the title.

19.03—Title and subtitle should be grammatically correct. Avoid faulty constructions and misplaced modifiers.

19.04—For capitalization, see **4.09, 4.12.**

19.05—When a drug is mentioned in the title or subtitle, use the approved generic name but omit the salt. (In special circumstances, eg, comparison of two forms of a drug or when the salt is integral to the name [eg, lithium carbonate], the salt may be included in the title.) Abbreviated drug names (eg, DMSO) are rarely acceptable (LSD is an exception). Trademarks should be avoided in titles, except in reports of the Department of Drugs or when the subject of the article is the formulation of a particular brand.

All drug names in titles and subtitles should be cleared with the Department of Drugs.

A drug mentioned in the title or subtitle should be included in the list of nonproprietary names and trademarks at the end of the communication. (See also **10.05/2, 10.05/4, 10.05/8.**)

19.06—For the use of numerals in titles and subtitles, follow **11.01-11.03** and **11.07-12.** At the beginning of a title, spell out all numbers and units of measure immediately following, as at the beginning of a sentence (**11.05-11.06**).

19.07—Species, subspecies, and the singular form of a genus name are italicized in title and subtitle. Do not italicize the name of a class, order, family, or tribe (eg, Mimeae).

Capitalize singular and plural forms of genus, class, order, family, and tribe. Do not capitalize species or subspecies (**10.07/4**).

19.08—For Greek letters in title or subtitle, follow the usage in the text: Do not

113

use capital letter (eg, B) if lower case (eg, β) is used in text. Capitalize the first non-Greek letter.

19.09—When quotation marks are needed in titles or subtitles, single quotation marks should be used. (See **14.12/5.**)

TYPOGRAPHY—20.00

Boldface—20.01

20.01/1—Boldface type should be used for center heads in the text and for run-in, first-order side heads.

REPORT OF A CASE

Prior Course

CASE 1.—

Comparison With Prior Experience.—

20.01/2—Punctuation following a boldface term should also be set boldface.

20.01/3—Column heads and major table divisions are set boldface.

Italics—20.02

20.02/1—Use italics to designate titles of books, periodicals and their abbreviations, proceedings, symposia, plays, long poems, musical compositions, space vehicles, planes, and ships. (See also **14.12/13, 20.03.**)

> *Mariner III*   SS *Hope*

> His plane was the *Betty Grable*.

20.02/2—Use italics to indicate a word, letter, or numeral used out of context. (See also **14.12/11.**)

> In his handwriting the *n*'s look like *u*'s.

> No punctuation is needed after *handwriting* in the sentence above.

20.02/3—Use italics *sparingly* to emphasize a word or phrase.

20.02/4—Italicize trademarks of drugs listed at the end of articles (**10.05/6**).

> Gallamine triethiodide—*Flaxedil*.

20.02/5—Italicize genus and species names (and abbreviations) of microorganisms, plants, and animals when used in the singular, either alone or in combination. Do not italicize the plurals or adjectival forms. Do not italicize class, order, family, or tribe names. Italicize name of variety or subspecies. (See also **10.07**.)

Streptococcus (*But:* streptococcal, streptococci)

20.02/6—Italicize foreign words and phrases that are not shown in *Webster's New Collegiate Dictionary* or in accepted medical dictionaries.

arrivederci   virginibus   puerisque

(*But:* in vivo)

20.02/7—Italicize the opening words in LETTERS TO THE EDITOR (See **14.05/4**.)

20.02/8—Italicize lowercase letters (and enclose in parentheses) when used to indicate divisions of enumeration in the text (**11.15**).

20.02/9—In the text and in references, italicize the name of the case in a legal citation. (See **15.42**.)

20.02/10—In resolutions, italicize *Resolved*. (*But* see **20.03/1**.)

20.02/11—In all mathematical formulas, and in other mathematical material in the text and tables, italicize letters used to designate unknown quantities, constants, lines, and variables. Do not italicize numerals or abbreviations (as for trigonometric functions and differential). (See **9.02**.)

$$y = ax + b \qquad \sin x = a/b$$

Small Caps—20.03

20.03/1—Each of the monthly specialty journals of the AMA Scientific Publications Division uses caps and small caps in the text to refer to itself (the ARCHIVES, the ARCHIVES OF DERMATOLOGY) and italics to refer to the other journals and *JAMA*. The weekly journal refers to itself in the italic acronym, *JAMA*, or as THE JOURNAL.

Note: Occasionally, it is necessary to give the full name for purposes of identification; in such a case, use italics: *The Journal of the American Medical Association*.

Use small caps alone for names of special departments within THE JOURNAL or the AMA specialty journals. (Do not use small caps when referring to an article rather than a department, eg, "In response to the editorial by John Smith, MD. . . .") Use caps and small caps for signatures in EDITORIALS, LETTERS, reviews in the BOOK FORUM, and QUESTIONS AND ANSWERS; for "WHEREAS" in resolutions (but italic for *Resolved*:); and for the designations "ED" in an editor's note. Use small caps for AM, PM, BC, AD.

20.03/2—In a type face that does not include small caps (eg, News Gothic, Futura, and most other sans serif faces), use caps for AM, PM, BC, and AD, but use caps and lowercase for the other items for which small caps or caps and small caps are specified in **20.03/1**.

UNITS OF MEASURE—21.00

All measurements in AMA scientific publications are given in metric units. English units are deleted routinely. However, English units may be given in those exceptional cases where conversion to metric would affect the precision of the measurement.

21.01—**Quantities**—Use Arabic numerals for all quantities (one or more) with units of measure except time (**11.03/J**).

21.02—**Abbreviations**—Most units of measure are abbreviated when used with numerals or in a virgule construction. (Correct abbreviations and specifications for their use are given in section **1.21**. See also **1.02** and **13.01**.)

Note that the prefix *pico-* is preferred to *micromicro*. For example, the picogram is preferred to the micromicrogram.

12.7 pg of calcium, not 12.7 $\mu\mu$g of calcium

Do not abbreviate units of measure when used with a spelled-out quantity, eg, at the beginning of a sentence (**11.06**).

Do not abbreviate units of time except in tables or in virgule constructions.

21.03—**Punctuation**—No punctuation is used between units of the same dimension.

4 ft 6 in   9 lb 2 oz

21.04—**Dosage**—Use metric values whenever possible. Avoid *teaspoonsful* and the apothecary *ounces, drams,* and *grains*. In some instances, *drops* is acceptable.

A large dose (50 mg) was administered.

The drug was given intravenously, 100 ml of a 2% solution at a rate of 30 drops per minute.

21.05—**Solution**—To show the strength of a solution in relation to normal, use the abbreviation "N" and constructions in accordance with these examples:

normal   N

twice normal	2N
half normal	0.5N or N/2

Note: A *molar* solution is one containing one gram molecule (mole) in 1,000 ml of solution. A *normal* solution is one having a concentration equivalent to 1 gm of solute per liter.

21.06—**Volume**—Use liters or subunits thereof to show measurements of liquids. For measurements of volume other than those of liquids, use cubic meters or multiples or fractions thereof.

A 45-cc jar was used.

About 50 ml of solute was needed.

The volume of the gas was reduced from 425 to 315 cc.

APPROXIMATE CONVERSIONS
TO METRIC MEASURES—21.07

Symbol	When You Know	Multiply by	To Find	Symbol
		Length		
in	inches	2.5*	centimeters	cm
ft	feet	30	centimeters	cm
yd	yards	0.9	meters	m
mi	miles	1.6	kilometers	km
		Area		
sq in	square inches	6.5	square centimeters	sq cm
sq ft	square feet	9.09	square meters	sq cm
sq yd	square yards	0.8	square meters	sq m
sq mi	square miles	2.6	square kilometers	sq km
	acres	0.4	hectares	ha
		Mass (Weight)		
oz	ounces	28	grams	gm
lb	pounds	0.45	kilograms	kg
	short tons (2,000 lb)	0.9	tonnes	t

*1 inch=2.54 cm (exactly).
Adapted from *Metric Conversion Card,* NBS Special Publication 365. US Dept of Commerce, National Bureau of Standards, July 1972.

UNITS OF MEASURE

Symbol	When You Know	Multiply by	To Find	Symbol
		Volume		
tsp	teaspoons	5	milliliters	ml
tbsp	tablespoons	15	milliliters	ml
fl oz	fluid ounces	30	milliliters	ml
c	cups	0.24	liters	liters
pt	pints	0.47	liters	liters
qt	quarts	0.95	liters	liters
gal	gallons	3.8	liters	liters
cu ft	cubic feet	0.03	cubic meters	cu m
cu yd	cubic yards	0.76	cubic meters	cu m
		Temperature (exact)		
F	Fahrenheit temperature	5/9 (after subtracting 32)	Celsius temperature	C

APPROXIMATE CONVERSIONS
FROM METRIC MEASURES—21.08

Symbol	When You Know	Multiply by	To Find	Symbol
		Length		
mm	millimeters	0.04	inches	in
cm	centimeters	0.4	inches	in
m	meters	3.3	feet	ft
m	meters	1.1	yards	yd
km	kilometers	0.6	miles	mi
		Area		
sq cm	square centimeters	0.16	square inches	sq in
sq m	square meters	1.2	square yards	sq yd
sq km	square kilometers	0.4	square miles	sq mi
ha	hectares (10,000 sq m)	2.5	acres	
		Mass (Weight)		
gm	grams	0.035	ounces	oz
kg	kilograms	2.2	pounds	lb
t	tonnes (1,000 kg)	1.1	short tons	

Adapted from *Metric Conversion Card*, NBS Special Publication 365. US Dept of Commerce, National Bureau of Standards, July 1972.

UNITS OF MEASURE

Symbol	When You Know	Multiply by	To Find	Symbol
		Volume		
ml	milliliters	0.03	fluid ounces	fl oz
liters	liters	2.1	pints	pt
liters	liters	1.06	quarts	qt
liters	liters	0.26	gallons	gal
cu m	cubic meters	35	cubic feet	cu ft
cu m	cubic meters	1.3	cubic yards	cu yd
		Temperature (exact)		
C	Celsius temperature	9/5 (then add 32)	Fahrenheit temperature	F

NORMAL CLINICAL LABORATORY VALUES*—21.09

Blood: Chemical Constituents	Range
Albumin, serum	4.0-5.2 gm/100 ml
Amino acids, serum (ninhydrin method)	3.5-5.5 mg/100 ml
Ammonia, serum	0.15-0.3 mg/100 ml
Amylase, serum (Myers and Killian)	< 50 units/100 ml
Ascorbic acid, serum	0.4-1.0 mg/100 ml
Base, total, serum	145-155 mEq/liter
Bilirubin, total, serum	0.1-0.8 mg/100 ml
Direct	0.1-0.2 mg/100 ml
Indirect	0.1-0.6 mg/100 ml
Calcium, serum	9-11 mg/100 ml
	4.5-5.5 mEq/liter
Carbon dioxide combining power, serum	50-65 vol%
	21-28 mEq/liter
Carbon dioxide content, serum	50-70 vol%
	21-30 mEq/liter
Carotenoids, serum	1-3 units/ml
Chlorides, serum (as Cl)	100-106 mEq/liter
	355-376 mg/100 ml
Chlorides, serum (as NaCl)	585-620 mg/100 ml
Cholesterol, total, serum (Schoenheimer-Sperry method)	120-260 mg/100 ml
Cholesterol as esters, serum	80-180 mg/100 ml
Cholesterol ester fraction of total cholesterol serum	60%-75%
Creatine (as creatinine) serum	1-2 mg/100 ml
Creatinine, serum	1-1.5 mg/100 ml

*Adapted from A. Smith and P. L. Wermer (eds): *Modern Treatment,* New York, Paul B. Hoeber, Inc, 1953.

Fat, neutral, serum	150-300 mg/100 ml
Fatty acids, serum	380-465 mg/100 ml
Fibrinogen, plasma	0.2-0.4 gm/100 ml
Globulins, serum	1.3-2.7 gm/100 ml
Glucose (fasting), blood	70-110 mg/100 ml
Hemoglobin, blood	
Males	14-18 gm/100 ml
Females	12-16 gm/100 ml
Icteric index, serum	4-7 units
Iodine, protein-bound, serum	4 μg-8 μg/100 ml
Iron, serum	80 μg-180 μg/100 ml
Lipase, serum	< 2 ml (0.05 N NaOH)
Lipids, total, serum	500-600 mg/100 ml
Magnesium, serum	2-3 mg/100 ml
	1.6-2.4 mEq/liter
Nitrogen, nonprotein, serum	15-35 mg/100 ml
Oxygen capacity, blood	18-22 vol%
Oxygen content, arterial blood	17-21 vol%
Oxygen content, venous blood, arm	10-16 vol%
Oxygen percent saturation, arterial blood	94-96 vol%
Oxygen percent saturation, venous blood, arm	60-85 vol%
pH, serum	7.37-7.45
Phosphatase, acid, serum (Gutman or King-Armstrong method)	1-4 units/100 ml
(Bodansky method)	0.2-0.8 unit/100 ml
Phosphatase, alkaline, serum	
(Bodansky method)	1-4 units/100 ml
(King-Armstrong method)	8-14 units/100 ml
Phospholipids, serum	175-275 mg/100 ml
Phosphorus, inorganic, serum	3-4.5 mg/100 ml
	1-1.5 mEq/liter
Phosphate clearance	17.1 ml/min
Potassium, serum	4.0-5.0 mEq/liter
Proteins, total, serum	6.5-8.0 gm/100 ml
Prothrombin, plasma (Quick method)	14-18 seconds, depending on thromboplastin used (70%-100%)
Sodium, serum	137-143 mEq/liter
Sulfates, inorganic, serum	0.5-1.5 mg/100 ml
Urea, serum	20-35 mg/100 ml
Urea, nitrogen, serum	10-25 mg/100 ml
Uric acid, serum	3.0-6.0 mg/100 ml
Vitamin A, serum	0.4-1.0 IU/ml

Blood: Clinical Examinations

Bleeding time	1-5 minutes
Clot retraction time	1-3 hours
Coagulation time	

Capillary blood	3-6 minutes
Venous blood	5-20 minutes
Formed elements	
Cells, differential count	
Lymphocytes	25%-35% (1,250-3,500/cu mm)
Monocytes	4%-10% (200-1,000 /cu mm)
Neutrophils	
Young (nonfilament)	3%-15% (150-1,500/cu mm)
Adult (filament)	50%-65% (2,500-6,500 /cu mm)
Eosinophils	0.5%-4% (25-400/cu mm)
Basophils	0.2% (0-200/cu mm)
Erythrocytes (red blood cells)	4,200,000-5,500,000/cu mm
Leukocytes (white blood cells)	5,000-10,000/cu mm
Platelets	200,000-500,000/cu mm
Reticulocytes	0.5%-2%
Erythrocytes	
Diameter, average	7.5 μ
Fragility	
Maximal resistance	0.32% NaCl
Minimal resistance	0.42% NaCl
Color index	0.9-1.1
Hematocrit	42%-50% (volume of cells)
Hemoglobin	
Adults, females	12.8-15.2 gm/100 ml
Adults, males	14-17 gm/100 ml
Children (varies with age)	10-18 gm/100 ml
Sedimentation rate	
Cutler: Men	2-8 mm
Women	2-10 mm
Rourke and Ernstene	< 0.4 mm/min
Westergren	< 15 mm/hr
Wintrobe: Men	0-9 mm/hr
Women	0-20 mm/hr
Volume, blood	70-100 ml/kg of body weight; 5.4 liters total blood volume for adult

Functional Tests

Sulfobromophthalein (Bromsulphalein)	No dye remaining in serum 45 minutes after injecting 5 mg/kg of body weight
Cephalin flocculation	No precipitate
Concentration and dilution	Specific gravity of urine after dry day 1.025 or more; after water day 1.003 or less
Creatine tolerance	70% ingested creatine retained in adults

Galactose tolerance — Excretion of not more than 3 gm of galactose in urine in five hours after ingestion of 40 gm of galactose

Glucose tolerance — Standard: After ingestion of 100 gm of glucose or 1.75 gm of glucose per kilogram of body weight, blood glucose level not more than 180 mg/100 ml after one-half hour and return to normal in two hours. Glucose not present in all urine specimens

Exton: One-half-hour blood glucose level not > 75 mg/100 ml higher than fasting glucose and one-hour value not more than 50 mg higher than in the one-half-hour specimen

Hippuric acid — Excretion of 3.0-3.5 gm of hippuric acid in urine in four hours after ingestion of 6.0 gm of sodium benzoate

Excretion of 0.70 gm of hippuric acid in urine in one hour after intravenous injection of 1.77 gm of sodium benzoate

Phenolsulfonphthalein — Intramuscular injection: 55%-75% in urine in two hours

Intravenous injection: 25% or more in urine in 15 minutes

Prothrombin test of liver function — Increase of 15% or more in the prothrombin concentration in the blood in 24-28 hours after the injection of synthetic vitamin K

Thymol turbidity test — 4 units

Urea clearance — 40 ml or more blood cleared per minute

75%-125% of average normal

Urine

Acidity, titratable — 200-500 ml N/10 alkali in 24 hours

Amino nitrogen — 0.4-1.0 gm/24 hr

Ammonia — 20-70 mEq/liter/24 hr

Calcium — 0.1-0.7 gm/24 hr

Creatinine — 1.0-1.6 gm/24 hr

"11—Oxysteroid" or "corticoids" (Formaldogenic method) — 0.5-2.0 mg/24 hr

Estrogens (Jailer method), Male — 5 μg-20 μg/24 hr

Female (nonpregnant) — 15 μg-100 μg/24 hr depending on time of menstrual cycle

Gonadotrophin (Levin & Tyndall) Male — 5-30 mouse uterine units/24 hr

Female — 5-100 mouse uterine units/24 hr depending on time of menstrual cycle

Pregnandiol
  (Marrian-Sommerville
   method)
    Male   0
    Female (nonpregnant)   3-10 mg/24 hr in second half of menstrual cycle
17-Ketosteroids
  (Holtorf-Koch method)
    Male   8-20 mg/24 hr
    Female   6-15 mg/24 hr
  Urobilin $< 1:20$ dilution
  Urobilinogen < 4.0 mg/24 hr

Cerebrospinal Fluid
  Cells < 5/cu mm, all lymphocytes
  Chlorides (as NaCl)   120-130 mEq/liter
  Colloidal gold test   Not more than one in any tube (ten tubes; each digit in curve represents one tube, eg, 0000000100)
  Glucose   45-65 mg/100 ml
  Protein   15-45 mg/100 ml
  Pressure   100-200 mm H_2O

Miscellaneous
  Basal metabolic rate -10% to $+10\%$
  Circulation time
    Calcium gluconate,   Average, 12.5 seconds; range 10-16 seconds
     arm to tongue
  Gastric test meal
    Free acid   24-45 degrees (each degree equals 1 ml of N/10 alkali per 100 ml of gastric fluid)
    Total acidity   50-100 degrees
    Volume   5-150 ml fasting
                   40-50 ml one hour after Ewald meal
  Respiratory quotient
    For burning
     carbohydrate   1.00
    For burning fat   0.71
    For burning protein   0.80
    Under basal conditions 0.83
  Venous pressure,
    peripheral vein   60-120 mm H_2O

editorial manual

COPY EDITING—22.00

Exactitude, judgment, and knowledge are qualities of the professional copy editor. Since copy editing is both art and science, those who would take on its responsibilities must become disciplined in those qualities, the better to recognize when something is wrong or unclear, to judge whether the copy should be altered, and to know how to effect the correction or clarification.

Since authors of manuscripts to be published in AMA scientific publications are usually sent edited typescripts and layouts for review instead of printers' proofs, copy editing is especially important in the production of those publications.

22.01—**Quality Review**—On receipt of each manuscript, a copy editor should review its contents for completeness and conformity to editorial requirements.

22.02—**Preparing Copy**—Although printers use some discretion in the handling of copy from the Scientific Publications Division, they are still obligated to set type the way copy is submitted. If the copy has simplified spelling, it will be set in this manner. Even if marks of punctuation are incorrect or words or proper names are misspelled, typesetters will almost invariably follow copy, because they are paid to be printers, not editors.

Alterations add to composition costs. Changes made *after* the original copy has been set in type become expensive. It is essential that copy be edited to its final form *before* it is sent to the printer. Printers correct their own errors at no charge to the publisher, but they do charge for the changes an editor makes in the printed copy.

Because authors do sometimes change their minds, they usually are sent edited typescripts, a layout, and a covering letter explaining the changes and asking for clarification of the text.

When the approved typescript is received from the author, the copy is rechecked to determine whether additions or deletions may have changed layout measurements.

Copy is then sent to the printer, who, after setting the type, arranges it on pages as indicated in the layout. When page proofs are made up, they are sent to the Proofreading Department for final checking.

Here are some general guidelines for preparing copy:

1. Edit the manuscript, *not* the proof. Corrections are costly on page proofs, even more costly on final proofs.

2. Follow specified style throughout. Be consistent. Be sure that data in illustrations and tables agree with those in the text.

3. Use subheads in text to break up solid columns in long articles. Subheads will help the reader to follow the development of the subject. They should enhance the meaning of the text.

4. All copy must be typewritten, and copy that has many changes or corrections must be retyped. It is sometimes acceptable to print legibly brief insertions or corrections. Be certain that all caps are used only when you want the printer to set all caps. If type is to be set uppercase and lowercase, print

copy that way or mark appropriately. Be sure all typewritten copy is double-spaced.

5. Number consecutively all pages of the manuscript (including references, tables, legends, footnotes) beginning with 1 on the title page. In addition, mark each page with the copy number and classification and, in specialty journals, a letter to identify the journal (eg, "D-1706-OC"). The senior author's name is often included for identification also.

6. As a guide for the Art-Layout and Production-Mark-Up Sections, indicate type size for various parts of the manuscript (eg, synopsis-abstract, case reports, references).

7. Make a copy of the edited typescript for insurance against loss and for a record of corrections and changes.

8. Mark the manuscript with your initials and the date before you release it for further processing.

COPY-EDITING MARKS—22.03

italics	published in the <u>New England Journal of Medicine</u>
boldface	Comment
capitals	National institutes of health
small capitals	BC 406
superscript	from Brown. ^{3} "Next, he shouted
subscript	CO_2
em dash	Latency.
en dash	Winston–Salem oriented study group
period	end of sentence
comma	red, blue, and green
semicolon	He was generous; he had the fault.
insert word(s)	a number of errors have been shown
changed word(s)	Things which that fall usually break.
lowercase a capital	He went East.
lowercase a cap series	CRITERIA FOR A PROFESSION

COPY EDITING

insert parens	Her pulse was normal (72 beats per minute).
plus	correlation coefficient was + 97.
minus	The value could not exceed −1.
hyphen	symptom‗free patients
paragraph	¶ Results of the survey showed an interaction.
insert colon	The briefest commandment is this: "Don't."
transpose elements	to only answer with his name
correct a "typo"	to spit⌃e his face, cut off ʰis noˢe.
delete elements	sat upon her tuffet; ~~there was~~ great anxiety ~~that~~ ensued
close up elements	an‿alysis
insert space	baseline#value
insert hyphen	follow‗up report
two-em dash	(item). ⊢2/M⊣ (next item)
insert thin space	P ⟨.05
mark Greek letter	μg/100 ml
indent one em	☐ Symptoms
indent two ems	⊡ Fever
flush left	⊏ Table stub
flush right	Signature ⊐
center element	⊐Subhead⊏
set as two lines, centered	⊐Gross and Microscopical⌐ Examination ⊏
set Roman	italic typeface and more italic typefacing
convert to alternate form	Two, ④, six, eight; the sum is twenty; 5 percent; a reaction (3 plus)

129

The sample page below has been edited. Note that the copy editor's markings, in contrast with the marginal markings of the proofreader (p 134), occur within the text of the typewritten page. A list of copy editing marks will be found on pp 128-129.

~~CASE~~ REPORT of a Case

¶ A
C. P., (twenty-three)=years=old, the mother of ③ children, was admitted to the hospital on Sept~~ember~~/ 15, 1960, following an illness of ④ days' duration. ¶ The illness ~~She~~ had started with a headache. One day ~~prior~~ before ~~to~~ admission, she ~~had~~ vomit~~ing~~ed and experienced ~~(weak+~~ ness in the left leg. ~~Cell count in the~~ cerebrospinal fluid at th~~e~~ time ~~was~~ at showed 20 WBC/ per cubic centimeter. She had had one ~~Salk~~ injection of poliomyelitis vaccine six months earlier.

At the time of admission, laboratory studies ~~showed~~ yielded the following values: hemoglobin, 12.4 grams/, 100 ml WBC, ~~white count~~ 8850/ cu mm, with 83 (percent) neutrophils, 15 (percent) lymphocytes, and 2% ~~per——cent~~ monocytes.

EDITING ILLUSTRATIONS—22.05

The author and editors should be cautious of every word appearing in the illustrations. This applies also to the legends. If an illustration has been used previously in another publication, written permission for its use must be obtained from the publisher and author. The source should be acknowledged, usually in a footnote at the end of the paper (**6.08**), occasionally in the legend (**8.07**).

Only good photographs should be used. Experience has led to the endorsement of the following principles:

1. Overreduction can destroy a good illustration and should be avoided.

2. Care should be taken not to make an illustration any larger than is necessary to convey its meaning.

3. Photomicrographs: If the scale must be changed, it should be noted in the legend. Staining technique should be given when appropriate.

4. The whole photo should not be used if a part tells the story.

5. In some cases it is advantageous to enlarge a portion of a photo to bring out a detail, rather than use the whole photograph.

Since most editors are not experts in layouts, most of this work is delegated to specialists in the Art and Layout Department. However, it is essential that editors have a general understanding of what can and cannot be done.

For example, even where individual cuts are required, it is often advisable to group photos. Advisability of such grouping depends on many factors, and the matter can generally be decided best by conference with the Art and Layout Department.

Never write on the surface or back of a photograph with a hard pencil or ballpoint pen; the markings will crease the emulsion and perhaps ruin the photo. Markings or writing should be placed on a tissue, which is then placed over the photo. Overlays affixed to photos and artwork protect them and also permit markings on the overlay to show how the photo or drawing is to be cropped, and areas that should be specified for more or less engraving tone density. Overlays may be of tissue or acetate.

LAYOUT AND PRODUCTION—23.00

23.01—**Layout and Type Specifications**—After the manuscript is edited, it goes to the Art and Layout Department where copy is estimated for length, illustrations are sized, and photostats are made for the illustrations. Repair and relettering (and, occasionally, original art) may be done by the Art-Layout Department at that time. The layout itself is then prepared, complete with affixed photostatic proofs of illustrations.

The layout, along with a copy of the edited typescript, is sent to the author to show the placement of the title, copy, illustrations, tables, and other parts as they will appear in page makeup. With copy and layout in hand, the author has the same materials that will be used to produce his article in published form.

After approval and return of the manuscript and layout by the author, the edited manuscript, layout, and illustrations are sent to the printer for typesetting and page makeup. Specifications to the printer on how to set type for given copy are usually written by the staff of the Production Department. Composition may be delayed when copy does not contain complete specifications. When printers have incomplete specifications, there are two alternatives: hold up the work and find out, or use imagination and furnish the missing specifications. One delays production; the other may result in work having to be reset.

Here is some information the printer must be given:

1. **Width of the column in picas.** Never use fractions of picas other than one half.

2. **Typeface.** Give the complete name. Examples: Century Expanded regular, bold, or italic; Vega medium; Helvetica bold.

3. **Size and leading.** To give the size of type is not enough. Leading, the space between lines, must also be specified. Example: *10/11 Century Expanded* means type of that face set in 10-point, with 1 point of space between each line. Ten alone or 10/10 means the face is to be set solid—with no extra space between lines.

4. **Paragraph indentions.** Indentions are usually 1 em of the type size for column measures up to and including 20 picas. An em is the square of the type body of any size. Within the text, a paragraph symbol will usually suffice to indicate paragraph indention. In tabular material, the usual indication to the printer is a square, with a figure inside if more than 1 em indention is desired. (See **22.03.**)

PROOFREADING—24.00

After copy has been set in type, proofs are pulled by the printer and are sent to the Proofreading Department. The original edited copy is attached to each proof for final checking. Errors in typesetting and incorrect statements or data should be corrected on proofs.

The proofreader follows copy and searches for errors. Appropriate symbols are used to indicate these mistakes in the margin space of the page or galley proofs. Some of the items a proofreader checks are (1) style inconsistencies, (2) spelling inconsistencies, (3) sequence of reference, figure, and table citations in the text, (4) discrepancies between the reference list, figure legends, or table data and the text, (5) grammatical errors, (6) printer's errors in typesetting (eg, type style, typeface, capitalization, punctuation, indentation, word division), and (7) positioning of copy, illustrations, legends, and tables according to the layout.

24.01—**Page Proofs**—Page proofs are presented as proof of page makeup—with all components of the composition in proper sequence and position.

Page proofs are advantageous in that they enable the staff to overcome space or makeup problems well in advance of press time.

All proofreader marks must be written in pencil in the margin. All corrections for printer to set in type must be printed. All directions to the printer that are not to be set in type should be written and circled.

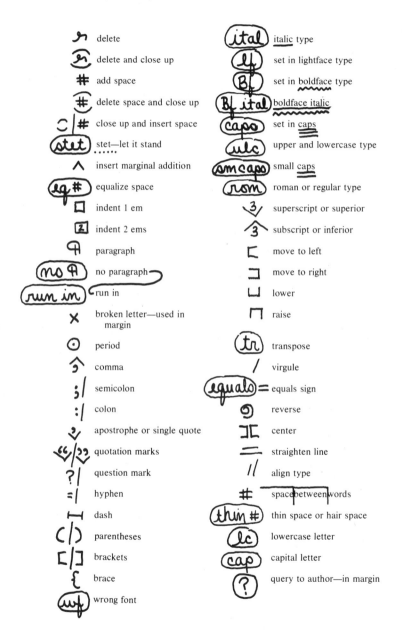

ℐ	delete	*ital*	italic type
	delete and close up	*lf*	set in lightface type
#	add space	*Bf*	set in boldface type
	delete space and close up	*Bf ital*	boldface italic
⌣ #	close up and insert space	*caps*	set in caps
stet	stet—let it stand	*ulc*	upper and lowercase type
∧	insert marginal addition	*sm caps*	small caps
eq #	equalize space	*rom*	roman or regular type
□	indent 1 em	3/	superscript or superior
2	indent 2 ems	3	subscript or inferior
¶	paragraph	⌐	move to left
no ¶	no paragraph	⌐	move to right
run in	run in	⊔	lower
×	broken letter—used in margin	⊓	raise
⊙	period	*tr*	transpose
⌃	comma	/	virgule
;/	semicolon	*equals* =	equals sign
:/	colon	⊙	reverse
⌄	apostrophe or single quote	⋺⋵	center
⌄⌄/⌄⌄	quotation marks	⎓	straighten line
?/	question mark	//	align type
=/	hyphen	#	space between words
⊢⊣	dash	*thin #*	thin space or hair space
(/)	parentheses	*lc*	lowercase letter
[/]	brackets	*cap*	capital letter
{	brace	?	query to author—in margin
wf	wrong font		

PROOFREADING SAMPLE—24.03

The following example shows how a proof is marked by the proofreader and how those corrections appear in the revised proof.

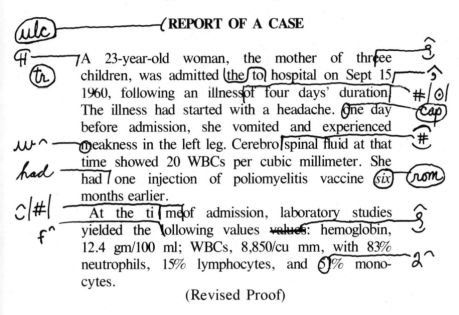

(Revised Proof)

Report of a Case

A 23-year-old woman, the mother of three children, was admitted to the hospital on Sept 15, 1960, following an illness of four days' duration. The illness had started with a headache. One day before admission, she vomited and experienced weakness in the left leg. Cerebrospinal fluid at that time showed 20 WBCs per cubic millimeter. She had had one injection of poliomyelitis vaccine six months earlier.

At the time of admission, laboratory studies yielded the following values: hemoglobin, 12.4 gm/100 ml; WBCs, 8,850/cu mm, with 83% neutrophils, 15% lymphocytes, and 2% monocytes.

COPYRIGHT—25.00

(which may be revised at any time), and thereafter are the property of the AMA. The law provides protection for 28 years, with renewal possible for an equal period.

To copy or reproduce in whole, without authorization from the copyright owner, constitutes a legal infringement. Permission to reprint the article, even by the author, must be obtained from the AMA. However, a reasonable type and amount of copying is permitted as "fair use" of a copyrighted work. No hard-and-fast rules exist to determine fair and unfair use. Each case depends on its own peculiar circumstances.

The most important factors to be considered in determining whether copying amounts to an infringement are (1) the quantity and value of the portion taken in relation to the works involved, and (2) the extent to which the copying may tend to supersede the original or interfere with its sale.

Greater tolerance as to copying is generally accorded scholarly works reproducing parts of earlier works, as necessary for all research and criticism. A good test to determine whether copying of a scholarly work constitutes an infringement is whether a reasonable copyright owner would consent to such use.

It is not permissible to quote an article in its entirety unless permission to do so is obtained in writing. In all cases, the quoted matter should carry a proper credit.

Example: Reprinted from *The Journal of the American Medical Association* (221:535-539, 1975). Copyright © 1975, American Medical Association.

Note that it is the *fact of publication* with a proper copyright notice that establishes copyright. Registration with the Copyright Office is merely a claim of copyright. If there is no notice on a published work, it may be assumed that there is no copyright.

International Copyright.—Under the Berne Convention (1886), works protected in one contracting nation are protected in each, according to its own laws. Most Western countries belong to this agreement, but the United States does not. However, its terms are generally respected by American publishers who expect similar treatment in the other countries. Under the UNESCO Universal Copyright Convention (1955), of which the United States is a signatory, protection in all participating nations is obtained by publication in any one, provided the proper notice is used (a "c" in a circle ©, the year, and the name of the copyright owner in the proper place, spelled out as shown earlier in this section).

Copyright Law.—Both domestic and international laws are often imprecise. They contain many exceptions and special conditions. The foregoing is meant to provide a general view of the subject, not a legal definition. It is a good idea to become familiar with current copyright requirements and to check whenever in doubt.

PHOTOGRAPHS

The copyright owner has a right to demand a fee for reproduction or to refuse permission altogether—and violation of copyright is punishable by law. Sometimes there is genuine doubt about the copyright status of a particular work. In such cases, inquiries should be made on the assumption that there is protection.

New Versions.—Under the Copyright Law (Title 17, US Code, Section 7) a new version of a copyrighted work that has been produced by the copyright owner or with his consent, is copyrightable as a "new work." Copyrightable "new works" include compilations, abridgements, adaptations, translations, and works republished with new material.

The copyright in a new version covers only the additions, changes, or other new material appearing for the first time in the work. Protection for a copyrighted work cannot be lengthened by republishing the work with new matter.

Reprints.—For the copyright to remain in force, it is essential that all published copies contain the correct statutory copyright notice. The form of this notice may vary depending on the nature of the work. No general rule can cover all possible situations, but the following should be considered:

The name of the copyright owner must be used in the credit line. The credit line must include the year date of original copyright registration, the word "Copyright", the abbreviation "Copr.", or the symbol ©, and, for Scientific Publications Division publications, the established wording approved for reprint credit notices.

PHOTOGRAPHS—26.00

In illustrations to be published by the AMA, where identification of a person is possible, written permission must be obtained from the person for use by the author in his article. Masking out the eyes in the picture is not a means for circumventing the need for such permission; the masking may, however, be a condition by the person for his granting permission to use his picture.

For pictures of minors (those less than 18 years of age) or wards, written permission must be obtained from both parents or from the legal guardian. If a parent is deceased, the permission of the surviving parent is sufficient. If parents are divorced, however, permission must be obtained from both for use of their child's picture.

The publication of a composite photograph of various family members necessitates that written authorization for use of the picture be obtained from each adult in the picture and from both parents (or guardian) of each child in the picture. The permission of the senior member of the family in such cases is definitely not sufficient.

INDEX

References are to section numbers.

INDEX

cg (centigram), 1.21
change word(s), copy-editing marks, 22.03
chapter(s)
   do not capitalize, 4.22
   numbers, 11.03C
chemical compounds and formulas
   brackets, braces, parentheses, 14.02/3, 14.02/4
   Greek letters, 7.04
   no legend for, 8.01
   periods omitted, 14.10/6
   used as adjectives, no hyphen, 14.08/4
chemical symbols
   isotopes, 10.10/2-10.10/4
   no periods, 14.10/6
χ^2 (chi square)
   statistics, 7.02
   symbol, 1.22, 17.01
children, correct usage, 5.07
ChM (master of surgery), 1.22
chromosome, do not capitalize, 4.22
chronic, correct usage, 5.02
churches, capitalization, 4.05
Ci (curie), 1.21
cigarette vs cigaret, 5.00 (intro)
circulation time, 21.09
circumflex accent, 2.02
cities
   acknowledgment footnotes, 6.08
   affiliations, 3.04, 3.05, 6.03
   capitalization of specific locations, 4.04
   organization name, 1.13
   place of publication, 15.26, 15.28
   without state or country name, 1.12
city, capitalization, 4.04
class (taxonomic)
   capitalization, 4.16, 19.07
   italics not used, 19.07, 20.02/5
classical references, 15.41
   Bible, 11.14, 14.03/6, 15.41
   numerals, 11.14, 15.41
clearance, correct usage, 5.11
clinical data
   abbreviations, 1.22
   laboratory values, 21.09
   values, correct usage, 5.11
clinical material, jargon, 5.05
clock referrals, 5.09, 11.03M
cm (centimeter), 1.21
CNS (central nervous system), 1.01, 1.22
co (company), 1.01, 1.08
Coast Guard, abbreviations, 1.19, 1.20
colon, 14.03
   between main clauses, 14.03/1
   between title and subtitle, 15.12
   biblical and classical citations, 14.03/6, 15.41
   capitalization after, 4.13, 14.03/2
   copy-editing marks, 22.03
   do not use, 14.03/4

enumerations, 4.13, 14.03/3
   introducing independent statements, 14.03/2
   proofreader's marks, 24.02
   quotations, 14.03/5
   ratios, 14.03/6
   references, 4.13, 14.03/7, 15.07, 15.15
   symbols and superscript reference citations before, 15.07, 18.08
   time of day, 11.03M, 14.03/6
color names, hyphenation, 14.08/3
colored, black preferred, 5.06
column(s)
   do not capitalize, 4.22
   marking widths, 23.01
   quoted material, reduced width, 14.12/3
   tables, 18.01, 18.03, 18.04, 18.09, 18.10, 20.01/3
comma, 14.04
   after opening clauses, long phrases, 14.04/1
   after place of publication, 15.28
   after suspended hyphens, 14.08/17
   before and, or, nor, 14.04/2
   before etc, 5.02
   copy-editing marks, 22.03
   in addresses, 1.14, 14.04/7
   in business names, 14.04/3
   in dates and expression of time, 14.04/8
   in numbers to indicate thousands, 14.04/9
   in reference citations, 15.07
   in series or enumerations, 14.04/2, 14.13/3
   in tables, 18.04
   inside footnote symbols, 18.08
   inside quotation marks, 14.04/12
   inside superscripts, 14.04/12, 15.07
   omitted before SE, SW, NE, NW, 1.14
   omitted between units of same dimension, 14.04/11
   omitted in proper names, 11.11
   omitted when *of* follows name of person, 14.04/7
   proofreader's marks, 24.02
   separate adjacent unrelated numerals, 14.04/10
   separate short clauses, 14.13/1
   to avoid mistaken junction, 14.04/1
   which, in nonrestrictive clauses, 4.02
   with academic degrees, 14.04/6
   with Jr and Sr, 1.05, 14.04/6
   with parenthetical conjunctions, adverbs, phrases, etc, 14.04/5
   with titles of persons, 14.04/6
   with viz, ie, eg, for example, 14.04/4
committee(s)
   capitalization, 4.03
   references, 15.24
company and manufacturers names
   abbreviations, 1.08

INDEX

physician's assistant, preferred to paramedic, 5.02
pico-, preferred to micromicro-, 1.21, 21.02
Pkwy (parkway), 1.14
Pl (place), 1.14
place of publication, 15.04, 15.26, 15.28, 15.32, 15.34
planes: See airplanes
plants, italics, 20.02/5
platelet factors, Arabic numerals for, 11.12
platonic, 4.07
plays
  capitalization, 4.09
  italics in, 20.02/1
plurals, 13.00
  abbreviations, 1.02, 13.01, 14.01/2
  apostrophe, 14.01/2-14.01/4
  capitalization, 1.02, 4.01, 4.03
  collective nouns, 13.02
  common nouns in titles of congresses, etc, 4.03
  compounds, 13.03
  genus and species, 4.16, 10.07/1, 10.07/5, 13.05, 20.02/5
  geographical names, 4.04
  italics not used, 20.02/5
  Latin and Greek vs English, 13.04
  letters of alphabet, 14.01/2
  numbers, 14.01/3
  organisms, 13.05
  street names, 1.14
  surnames, 14.01/4
  symbols, 14.01/5
  units of measure, 13.02
  words spoken of, 14.01/2
plus, copy-editing marks, 22.03
PM (post meridiem), 1.22, 20.03/1
  numbers with, 11.03M
PNH (paroxysmal nocturnal hemoglobinuria), 1.22
PO (post office), 1.22
Po₂ (oxygen pressure [tension]), 1.22
PodD (doctor of podiatry), 1.22
poetry
  italics in, 20.02/1
  short, quotation marks for titles, 14.12/13
  virgule in dividing run-in lines, 14.14/2
political divisions, capitalization, 4.04
political doctrines, not capitalized, 4.05
political parties, capitalization, 4.05
population, mean of, statistical symbol, 17.01
possessions of US, abbreviations, 1.11
possessives
  apostrophe in, 14.01/1
  eponyms do not take, 4.08, 5.01
  hyphen in, 14.08/10
  references, 15.08

pound
  abbreviation, 1.21
  conversion tables, 21.07, 21.08
pp (pages), 1.02, 1.22
PPD (purified protein derivative), 1.22
ppm (parts per million), 1.21
predominant vs preponderant, 5.02
prefixes
  capitalization, 4.12
  hyphenation, 14.08/11-14.08/16
  isotopes, 10.10/8
  names of persons, 15.09
preparation of copy, 22.02
preponderant vs predominant, 5.02
prepositions
  capitalization, 4.03, 4.09, 15.10
  in compound nouns, 14.08/9
  no colon after, 14.03/4
  prepositional phrases
    danglers, 5.13
  "per" construction, 14.14/1
prepped, jargon, 5.05
presented with vs had, 5.06
president, capitalization, 4.02
prevalence vs incidence, 5.02
prime
  do not use apostrophe, 14.01/5
  omitted in complement no., 10.02
printer, specifications for, 23.01
printout: See drug nomenclature printout
probability, statistical symbol, 1.22, 17.01
proceedings, italics, 20.02/1
proofreading, 24.00
  marks, 24.02
  page proofs, 24.01
  sample, 24.03
proper nouns
  capitalization, 4.01
  hyphen, 14.08/12
  Roman numerals with, 11.11
  Saint and Saints, 1.10
  words derived from, 4.01, 4.07
proprietary names: See trademarks
psi (pounds per square inch), 1.21
psia (pounds per square inch absolute), 1.21
psig (pounds per square inch gauge), 1.21
PSRO (Professional Standards Review Organization), 1.22, 13.01
psychiatric floor, jargon, 5.05
pt (part), 1.22
pt (pint), 1.21
PTC (plasma thromboplastin component), 1.22
publishers, 1.08, 14.04/3, 15.26-15.28
  See also company and manufacturers names
Publisher's Trade List Annual, reference source, 15.27
punctuation, 14.00
  apostrophe, 14.01

INDEX

INDEX

section
do not capitalize, 4.22
foreign words, 15.43
section mark in tables, 18.08
self-, hyphen with, 14.08/15
SEM (standard error of the mean), 1.22,
17.01
semicolon, 14.13
complex enumeration, 14.13/2
compound sentence, 14.13/1, 14.13/2
copy-editing marks, 20.03
in by-lines, 3.03
outside superscript reference citation,
15.07
proofreader's marks, 24.02
symbols before, 18.08
with conjunctive adverb, 14.13/2
SErD (skin erythemal dose), 1.22
serial publications, references, 15.33
series
Arabic numerals, 11.07
comma, 14.04/2
company names, 14.04/3
do not capitalize word, 4.22
hyphen, 14.08/17, 15.07
legal citations, 15.42
percent, 12.01
See also enumerations
serology was negative, jargon, 5.05
sex referents, 5.07
SGOT (serum glutamic oxaloacetic
transaminase), 1.01, 1.17, 1.22
SGPT (serum glutamic pyruvic
transaminase), 1.22
ships
capitalization, 4.09
italics, 20.02/1
sic, 14.02/1, 14.12/7
sideheads
boldface type, 20.01/1
capitalization, 4.11, 4.12
dash, 14.05/1
Greek letters, 7.03
hyphenated compounds, 4.12
periods, 14.05/1, 14.10/5
siemens, do not abbreviate, 1.21
Σ (sum, summation), 1.22, 7.02, 17.01
σ (standard deviation), 17.01
σ^2 (variance, population), 17.01
s_2, statistics, 7.02, 17.01
signatures
caps and small caps, 3.04, 3.05, 20.03/1
military titles, 1.19, 1.20, 3.04, 3.05
significant(ly), correct usage, 5.02
skull series, jargon, 5.05
slash accent, 2.02
small capitals, 20.03
AM, PM, BC, AD, 1.22, 20.03/1
AMA publications, 15.23, 20.03/1
copy-editing marks, 22.03
proofreader's marks, 24.02

signatures, 3.04, 3.05, 20.03/1
special depts of AMA publications,
15.23, 20.03/1
type face not including, 20.03/2
WHEREAS, in resolutions, 20.03/1
Social Security Act, capitalization, 4.06
societies
"read before" footnotes, 6.05
references to proceedings, 15.22
references to unpublished material read
before, 15.39
solution, strength, 21.05
songs: See musical compositions
space vehicles, italics, 20.02/1
spacing
abbreviations, 1.00
after suspended hyphen, 14.08/17,
14.08/18
author initials in references, 15.08
insert or close up, copy-editing marks,
22.03
insert or close up, proofreader's marks,
24.02
percent symbol, 12.01
quotations, 14.12/3
reference citations, 15.07, 15.15
states, territories, possessions,
abbreviations, 1.11
special collections, references, 15.35
special materials, references, 15.32-15.43
audiotapes, 15.38
classical references, 15.41
Congressional Record, 15.36
Federal Register, 15.36
foreign words of reference, 15.43
government bulletins, 15.32
legal references, 15.42
quotations, 15.40
secondary citations, 15.40
serial publications, 15.33
special collections, 15.35
statutory publications, 15.37
theses, 15.34
unpublished material, 15.39
videotapes, 15.38
specialty journals
caps and small caps, and italics, 20.03/1
running feet, 16.00, 16.03
special departments, 15.23
species: See genus and species
spelling, correct usage, 5.00 (intro)
sq cm, ft, in, m, mm (square. . .), 1.21
Sr (senior), 1.05, 14.04/6, 15.08
SS (Saints), 1.10
SSA (Social Security Administration),
1.22
SSD (source-skin distance), 1.22
SSU (Saybolt seconds universal), 1.21
St (Saint), 1.10
St (street), 1.14
stage, do not capitalize, 4.22